G000056925

belair

Curricular-Links

Science 5

Carolyn Dale

Acknowledgements

To everyone in the following Maidenhead primary schools who worked so hard to meet deadlines and to produce work of such a high quality for this book, a big, big thank you.

Lowbrook, Knowl Hill, St Edmund Campion RC, Claires Court Schools, The Ridgeway, Waltham St Lawrence, White Waltham C of E and Woodlands Park and to Juniper Hill Primary School, Flackwell Heath, Marlow. Without them there would be no book at all!

A very special big thank you to Mary Gallop and Jean Davies of Lowbrook School who enthusiastically produced so much work for the book and lent their delightful children to try out some of the activities; to Marion Bintcliffe and Judy Nott of The Ridgeway for their enthusiasm and willingness to take on extra work at the last minute so that we could complete displays on time; to Shirley Craddock, a talented and creative ex-colleague who worked tirelessly in putting finishing touches to displays; to Zoë Parish, Paul Naish and Steve Forest for their patience and advice, and thank you to Claire O'Neill.

And last, but by no means least, my family and friends who have had to live with these books for a long time. I do hope that everyone – friends, family and colleagues appreciate the final result!

From Keeping Healthy on page 14

© 2008 Folens on behalf of the author.

Belair Publications, Waterslade House, Thame Road, Haddenham, Buckinghamshire HP17 8NT.

Email: belair@belair-publications.co.uk

Belair Publications are protected by international copyright laws. All rights reserved.

The copyright of all materials in this publication, except where otherwise stated, remains the property of the publisher and author. No part of this publication may be reproduced, stored in a retrieval system, or transmitted, in any form or by any means, for whatever purpose, without the written permission of Belair Publications.

Carolyn Dale hereby asserts her moral right to be identified as the author of this work in accordance with the Copyright, Designs and Patents Act 1988.

Commissioning Editor: Zoë Parish
Page Layout: Barbara Linton
Editor: Rob Linton
Photography: Steve Forest
Cover Design: Sophie Pelham
Illustrations: Martin Pierce

First published in 2008 by Belair Publications.

Every effort has been made to trace the copyright holders of material used in this publication. If any copyright holder has been overlooked, we should be pleased to make the necessary arrangements.

British Library Cataloguing in Publication Data. A catalogue record for this publication is available from the British Library.

ISBN 978-1-84191-465-7

EAT
A DAY
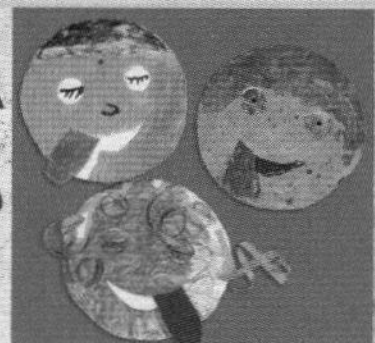

février
décembre

EAT
A DAY
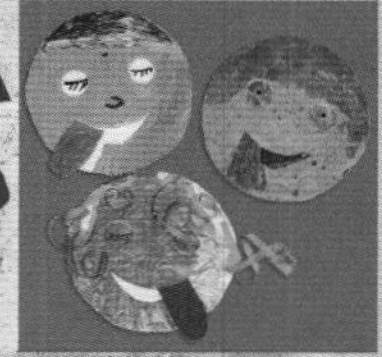

février
décembre

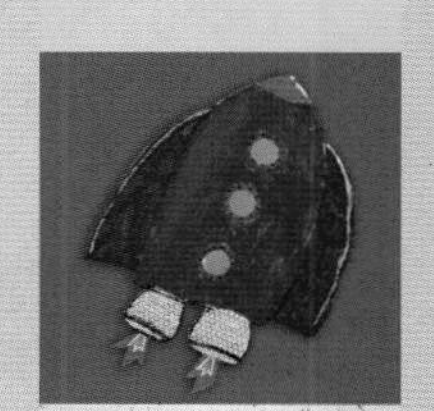

février
décembre
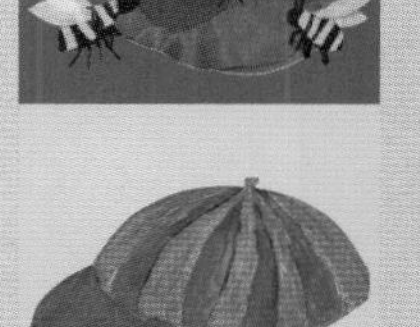

février
décembre

Contents

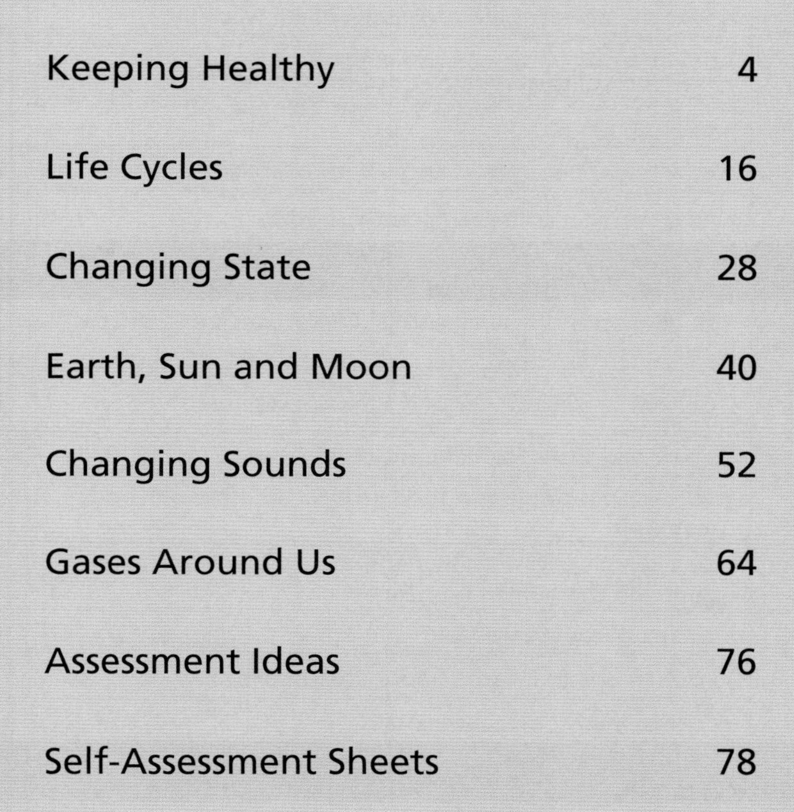

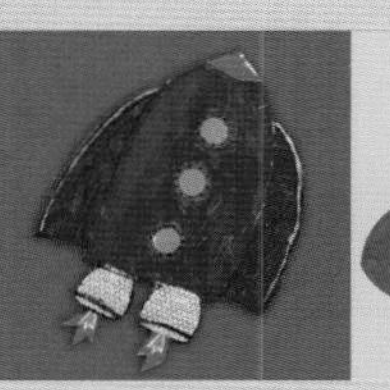
EAT
A DAY

février
décembre

EAT
A DAY

Keeping Healthy

These grids demonstrate the learning objectives covered in the activities within the theme. The curriculum references indicate the relevant programme of study (PoS) for a subject area unless otherwise stated.

	Learning Objectives	Curriculum References
Science (Page 6)		
Scientific Enquiry	Repeat measurements of pulse and breathing rates for accuracy.	Sc1/2g
	Recognize when to use line and bar graphs (link with numeracy).	Sc1/2f,h
	Extract information about pulse and breathing rates from line graphs (link with numeracy).	Sc1/2h-j
Life Processes and Living Things (QCA Science Unit 5A)	Know the different life processes of animals.	Sc2/1a
	Know that diet and exercise affect health.	Sc2/2b,h
	Know parts of the body and their functions, including the heart and lungs.	Sc2/2c
	Know how pulse rate changes with exercise.	Sc2/2d
	Know the effects of drugs on the body.	Sc2/2g
Literacy (Page 8)		
Speaking	Ask questions of a professional person, such as a doctor, nurse or nutritionist.	En1/2b
Listening and Responding	Consider arguments for and against exercise.	En1/1a-f;3a-f
Group Discussion	Debate the cases for different diets.	En1/1a-f;3a-f
Understanding and Interpreting Texts	Find out about different food groups and how our body uses them.	En2/3a-g
	Use a search engine to find answers to questions about health and the human body.	ICT PoS 1a-c;5b
Creating and Shaping Texts	Devise poems about health.	En3/1a-e;2a-f
	Write an imaginary text about a vegetable.	En3/1a-e;2a-f
	Write epitaphs for centenarians.	En3/1a-e;2a-f
Mathematics (Page 10)		
Using and Applying Mathematics	Calculate the cost of tee shirts.	Ma2/1a-d;4a,b; ICT PoS 1a-c; QCA ICT Unit 5D
	Collect information about the cost of different biscuits/ other foods.	Ma2/1a-d;4a,b
	Use spreadsheets to devise menus and calculate their cost.	Ma2/1a-k; ICT PoS 1a-c; QCA ICT Unit 5D
Handling Data	Measure pulse rates and complete a table.	Ma4/1a;2b,c
	Convert information to a line graph.	Ma4/1a;2b,c
	Interpret a line graph and a bar graph.	Ma4/2b,c
	Recognize when to represent data in a line or bar graph.	Ma4/2b,c
	Make a spreadsheet about fruit and vegetables.	Ma4/1a,c,d,e,f;2a,b,c,f; ICT PoS 1a-c;2a; QCA ICT Units 5C & 5D

Keeping Healthy

Learning Objectives	Curriculum References
PSHCE (Page 12)	
Find the possible combinations for eating five-a-day.	PoS 1a;3a
Recognise features of a healthy lifestyle.	PoS 1a;2a;3a,b; QCA Citizenship Unit 02
Evaluate own lifestyle and propose changes.	PoS 2f;3a
List school rules about health and safety.	PoS 2b;5d
Find out about foods eaten by different cultures.	PoS 4b
Geography (Page 12)	
Consider how and where we spend our time.	PoS 1b,c
Diets in other parts of the world and health issues there, e.g. Mediterranean, Inuit and Japanese diets.	PoS 3a-g
History (Page 12)	
Compare breakfast/dinner in the past and present, and feelings about them.	PoS 2c
Design & Technology (Page 14)	
Design a new healthy food and packaging for it.	PoS 1a-d;2a-f;3a-c;4a-c;5a-c
Design a slogan and picture for a tee shirt to promote health in school.	PoS 1a-d;2a-f;3a-c;4a-c;5a-c
Make a face that has a moving tongue (link with science).	PoS 1a-d;2a-f;3a-c;4a-c;5a-c
Design menus for healthy and not so healthy meals.	PoS 1a-d;2a-f;3a-c;4a-c;5a-c
MFL (Page 14)	
Know names of foods and how to ask for them.	PoS 1a-d;2a-c;3a-g; QCA MFL Unit 8
Art (Page 14)	
Make observational sketches of different foods.	PoS 1a-c
Music (Page 14)	
Listen to music with a beat (like the heart).	PoS 3a;4a,b
Devise lyrics with a beat and accompany with tuned rhythms.	PoS 1a-c; QCA Music Unit 19
PE (Page 14)	
Describe different sports and how they benefit us.	PoS 4a-c
List types of exercise and the effect on different parts of our bodies.	PoS 2a-c;4a-d
Respond to challenges that improve aspects of fitness.	PoS 10a-c

Science

Starting Points

- Find out about the children's ideas regarding their heart and lungs and their functions. Ask them to cut out the shape and size of their heart and lungs from paper, and then write what they think the function of each organ is on the cut-outs.
- Ask them to pin the shapes on their bodies where they think they are. Compare the children's ideas so they begin to consider how correct they are.

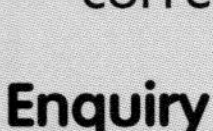

Enquiry

- Teach the children how to measure their pulse and breathing rates. Repeat for accuracy. Provide a table such as the one below as a guide. See the activity sheet on page 7.

Activity	Sitting still	Throwing and catching a ball with a partner for 1 minute	Walking on the spot for 1 minute
Beats per minute			
Breaths per minute			

Compare the results and make up a class database. How much variation is there? Can they find any patterns in results?

Extension Activities

- Discuss with the children what they need to do to keep as healthy as possible – food, exercise, amount of sleep, hygiene. Ask them to draw a body that is not so healthy and write labels about lifestyle. Are the children overly concerned about image rather than what is and what is not healthy?
- List different types of exercise. Display pictures of them with labels to show how they are good for us.
- Take pulse and breathing rates before and during games lessons and carrying out other activities. Which activities make them breathe the hardest and make their pulse rates go the highest? Find out what happens to the pulse rates of very fit athletes when they exercise. Set targets to improve fitness.

SAFETY!
YOU NEED TO DECIDE IF CHILDREN WITH HEALTH PROBLEMS SHOULD DO EXERCISES WHICH RAISE THEIR PULSE RATES SIGNIFICANTLY.

- Discuss drugs (find out local advice on this or invite a health specialist to give a talk); which drugs do children take – aspirin, asthma inhalers and so on. Talk about how these help us to stay healthy. Find out about other drugs that help people. Talk about the dangers of taking them without permission from an adult, as too much can be harmful. Discuss where they are kept and how lids ensure protection from children. Discuss harmful drugs and what they can do to a healthy body.

Ready, steady, go!

It's a fact! To run fast you need healthy lungs and a healthy heart.

Work with a partner.

Time your pulse and breathing rates like this:

1. Count the number of beats in 15 seconds and multiply it by 4 for beats per minute. Place the fingers of one hand on your other wrist, as shown in the diagram. Move your fingers around until you can feel a pulse.
2. Count the number of breaths you take in a minute. Try to breathe normally. Compare your results with three other people.

My pulse rate is ☐ per minute.

My breathing rate is ☐ per minute.

Now try!

Compare your pulse and breathing rates before and after a race.

1. Do an exercise for 2 minutes. What happens to both your pulse and breathing rates?

   ____

2. Time how long it takes for your pulse and breathing to get back to normal.
3. Tell your partner why your pulse and breathing rates go up after exercise.

NOW!

What other changes do you notice when you exercise?

____

____

____

Write five facts about your heart and five facts about your lungs.

Literacy

Speaking and Listening

- Practice a steady beat, like a heartbeat. Using a title about the heart/breathing/health, make up a word to chant to it. Add words together to make a group chant. Develop into phrases, then sentences and poems to say and/or write.
- Hold a class debate – one person to speak for and one to speak against topics such as chips on the menu at lunchtime, the importance of exercise or staying up to watch TV until you want to go to bed. Each person should try to persuade the class to vote for their idea.
- Make a statement to promote discussion: 'Joe only eats chips and baked beans'. What do children think about this diet? Will he stay healthy? Debate the cases for different diets. How healthy is a vegetarian diet? Is it dangerous to cut out certain foods?
- Devise questions to ask a professional person such as a doctor, nurse or nutritionist. If possible, invite one to school. If not, make up an interview and record it.

Eat a Rainbow Every Day!

Eat a rainbow everyday;
Help keep colds and coughs at bay!
Every colour you can see,
Try to eat them naturally.

Raspberries, red
And berries, blue.
Peppers, yellow
Green and red too!
Aubergines, purple,
Grapefruit, pink.
Name an orange fruit?
"Let me think!"

Eat a rainbow everyday;
We know that's the healthiest way!

Reading and Writing

- Make up names of people who lived until they were 100 years old. Decide how each managed to stay fit and healthy until that age. Write an epitaph for them, for example:

'Here lies Wendy Wizard **Born .... died ....** **Rode her bicycle to the shop every day.'**	**'Don Digger** **Grew his own vegetables in his allotment** **The best and biggest carrots in the county.'**

  Extend into more detailed information in writing an obituary for a newspaper, as in the display above

- Devise food characters and find out how eating them affects health and well-being. Use the activity sheet on page 9 to create poems like the one shown on the display above.
- Use a search engine to find answers to the children's questions about health and the human body. Useful websites for facts, activities and games are:

  www.sleepforkids.org/

  www.teenshealth.org/kid/

Good enough to eat!

Agnes Apple

I am bursting full of good things!
Just one taste of me
And your skin will glow,
Your face will be rosy,
Your hair will shine.
I am so beautiful!

Clarissa Cake

Ooh! Don't you just love me.
Oozing with cream,
So, so sweet.
I love to meet everyone.
Eat lots of me and guess what?
You won't stay beautiful for long!
Rotten teeth, spots.
Hah, hah, hah!

Here are two more characters!

Brian Banana's fact file

Bananas are good for you. Sportsmen often eat them during a match to give them energy

Clarence Crisp's fact file

Crisps are full of salt and fat. Your body doesn't need very much of these each day. If you eat too many of these, you will not be very healthy.

Draw one of them.

Use the fact file to make up a verse like the ones above.

Make up some other food characters. But find out about them first!

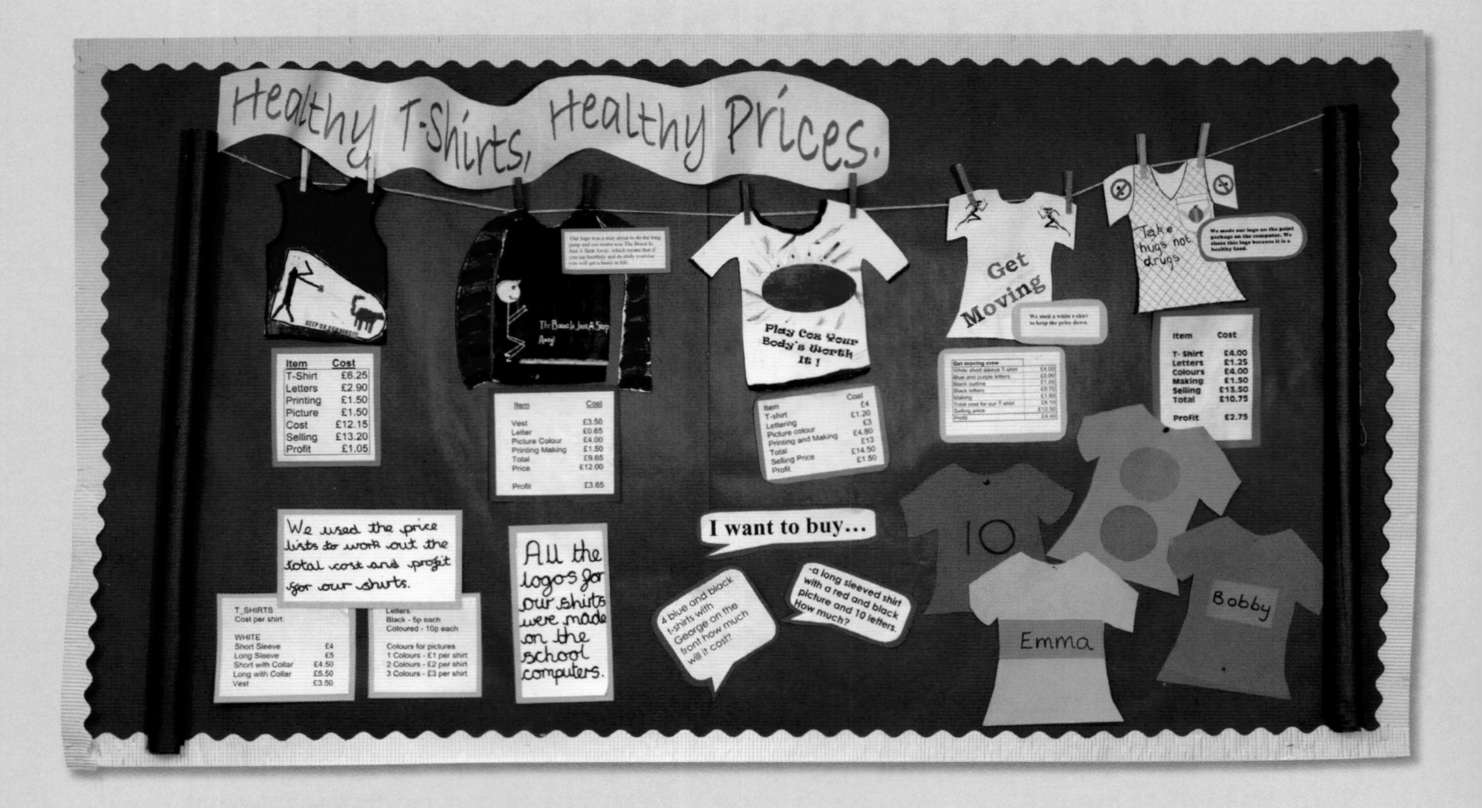

Maths

Using and Applying

- On paper, devise a suitable logo for a 'fit club'. Transfer it to the computer and use a graphics programme to display it in colour. Use the selected logo on posters to help the school become a healthier place.
- Ask the children to design a tee shirt. Decide on the cost for different sizes; one/two/three colours; long or short sleeves and so on. Calculate the cost of their tee shirt. Create questions about them – for example, working out the cost of identical tee shirts for a family. Use a spreadsheet to calculate costs, and display as shown above.
- Ask the children to make up a menu for a balanced meal. Calculate its cost. Compare the cost with a fast food meal, or work out the difference between using organic and non-organic food.
- Find some healthy recipes, and discuss why they are good for us. Make one. Weigh the ingredients. Calculate the cost of preparing the recipe for a family or the entire class.

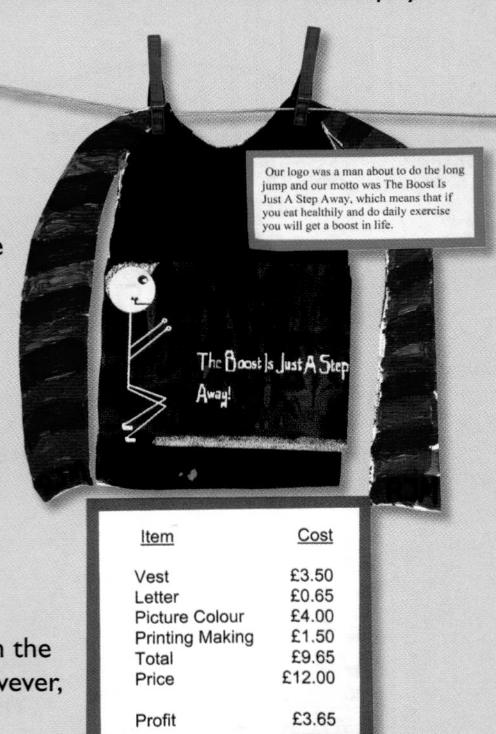

Handling Data

- Collect information about the cost of fruit and vegetables. Ask the children to find the difference in price between buying organic and non-organic vegetables, and to create a spreadsheet to show the results.
- Convert pulse and breathing rates to a line or bar graph. Discuss which is the most appropriate. Devise questions and interpret information from the graphs, as on the activity sheet on page 11.
- Devise databases containing information about aspects of children in the class or school – include measurements and aspects of lifestyle. However, be sensitive to children's feelings about height and weight.

What's Joe been doing?

This is Joe's pulse rate during different activities in the day.

Write the correct letter under each bar to show what his pulse was when doing different things:

A running in the playground

B sitting at his desk

C walking to the hall

D sleeping

E throwing a ball for the dog to fetch

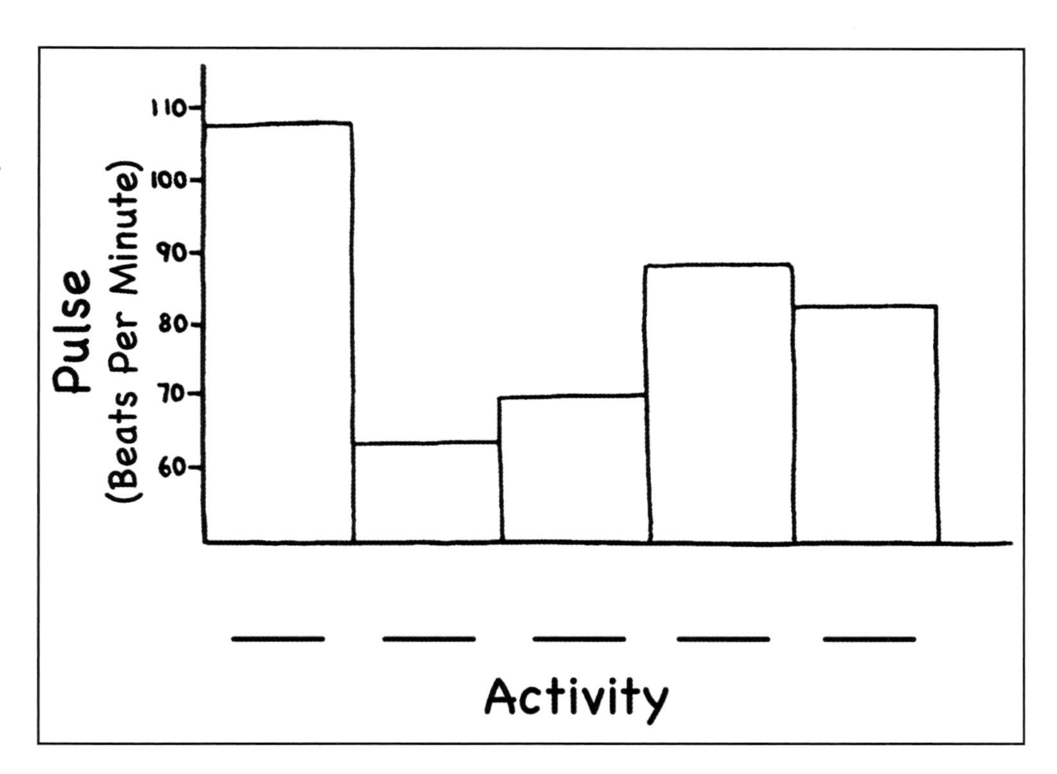

This is more difficult:

The line graph shows how Joe's breathing rate changed during a cross country run.

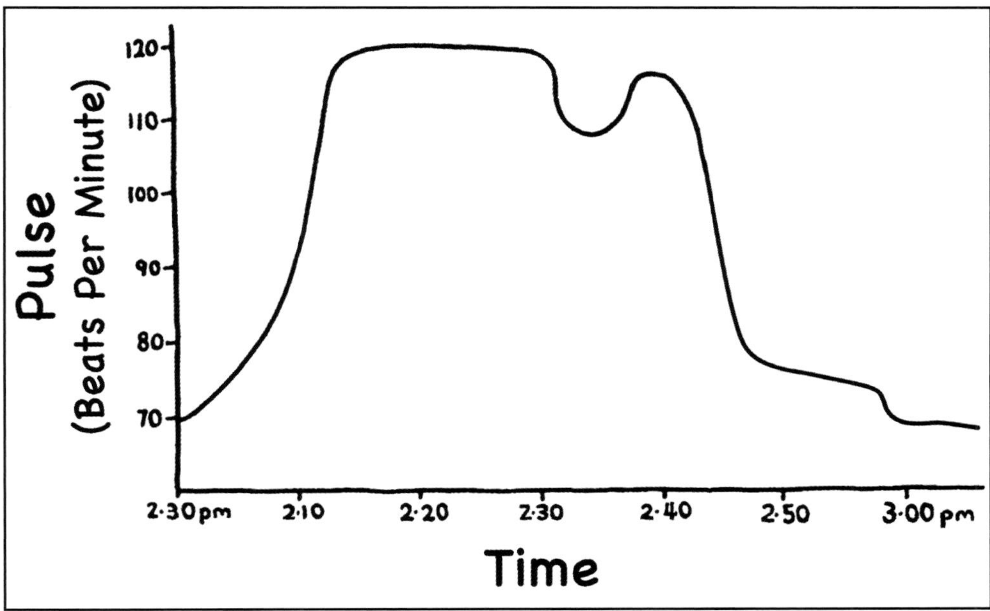

1 What was Joe's breathing rate at the start? __________

2 What was his highest breathing rate? __________

3 At what time did it get back to normal? __________

4 What do you think he was doing between 2:30 pm and 2:40 pm?

____

____

PSHCE

- Talk about what we mean by eating five-a-day. List ways of eating fruit and vegetables – as fruit drinks, cooked, raw and so on. Draw them, and make up a collage of the variety as shown. This could be sorted into colour bands to show the variety of colours available. Everybody should eat some fruit and vegetables from each colour band of the rainbow as each different coloured fruit and vegetable contains different minerals and vitamins for health. See the activity sheet on page 13 for more aspects of keeping healthy.
- List school rules about health and safety. Do children think some are unnecessary? Are there others they think should be included?

Geography

- Consider how and where we spend our time. To stay healthy and well, which activities should we do less of and which more? Link with PSHCE. Ask children to mark aspects of their own life from 1 to 10 – how often they exercise (this could be split into categories such as running, walking, playing sport, swimming etc), how many fruit and vegetables they eat each day, how much water they drink, how often they brush their teeth and so on. Children to set targets for themselves:

  I should do less of ....
  Once a week, I will ....
  3–5 times a week I will ....
  As often as I can I will ....
  Every day I will ....
  I will eat less of ....
  I will eat more of ....

- Find information about people in another part of the world. For example, Japanese people live longer and healthier lives than people in Europe. Ask the children to find out about their way of life and suggest reasons for this. Other comparisons could be made between the UK and Mediterranean countries, or the Inuit and western countries.

History

- Ask the children to find out about scurvy, a disease affecting sailors in Tudor times, and the work of Dr James Lind (1716–1794) who found out how to stop it happening.
- Find out what great-grandma and great-grandad had for breakfast or dinner. How is it different from today? Was their diet less or more healthy than ours? Discuss how diet and exercise affected their health and the strength of their bones and muscles. Find out what frozen foods were available then. How did rationing affect their lives? Try to show a real ration book. Compare other aspects of life now and in 1948, such as daily food intake and amount of exercise.

Energetic Ernie!

This is Energetic Ernie. He is really healthy.

Colour and decorate his body to show what he looks like.

Around him, put labels about his lifestyle:

- What he eats.
- How he exercises and how often.
- How he keeps clean.
- How much sleep he has.

Can you think of anything else?

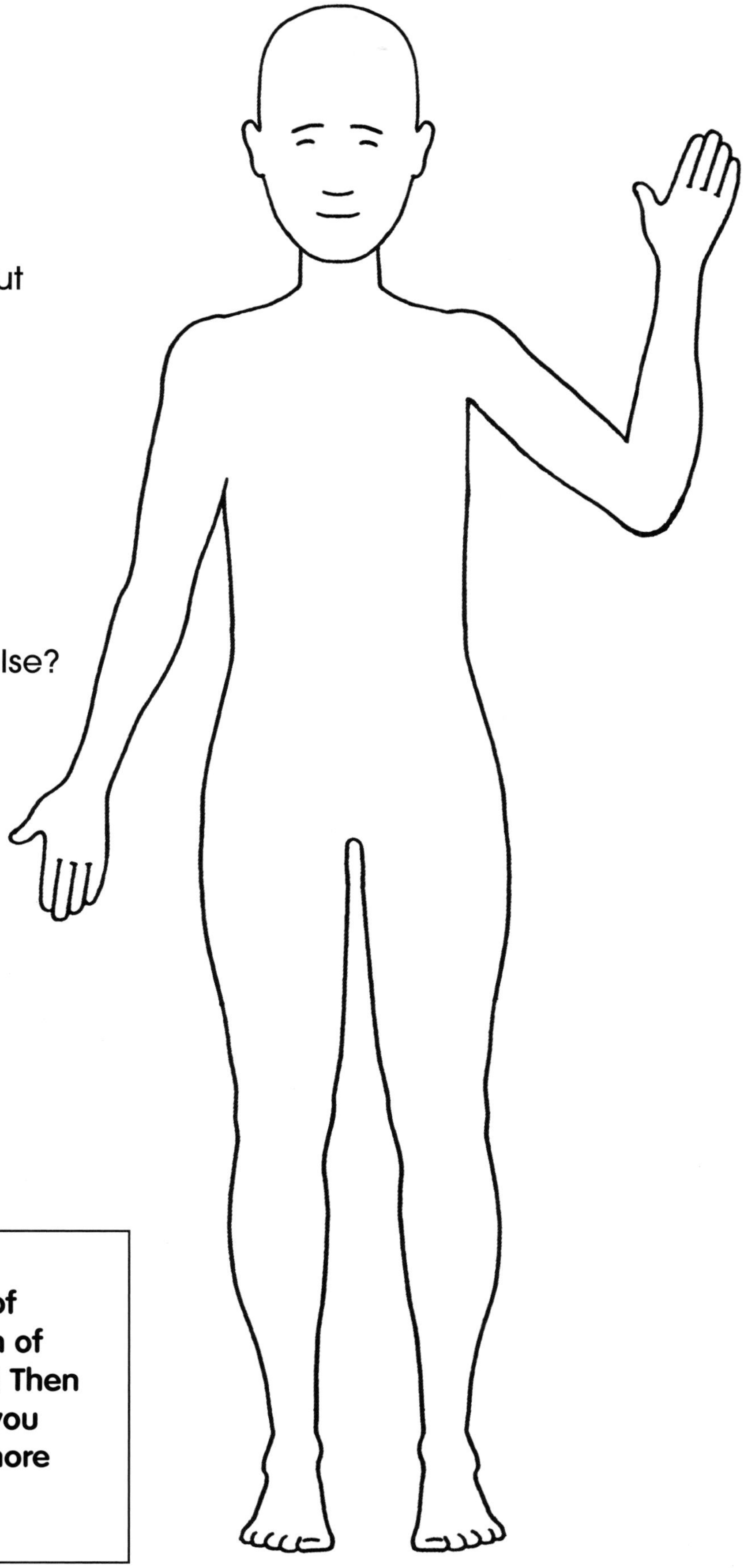

NOW!

Draw another outline of him and draw the path of food through his body! Then research to find out if you are correct, and add more information.

Art

- Carefully observe the outside and inside patterns and textures of fruit and vegetables. Shape, stick and stitch a variety of textured materials to represent them.
- Make observational sketches of different foods. Use a variety of materials such as pencils, charcoal, chalks, pastels and paints. Ensure that the surface texture matches the real thing – shiny or matt, bumpy or smooth and so on.

Design & Technology

- Carry out a survey of which snacks children in the class/school like best. Evaluate how healthy they are. Can children design an alternative that is a healthy snack – not too much sugar, salt or fat? Have a class vote to decide on the best ideas. Decide on shape and size, and design attractive packaging for it. There should be an opportunity to revise types and amounts of materials for packaging.
- Carry out a crisp survey – ask 'crisp questions' and design a healthy crisp that is also tasty and attractive to children. See the activity sheet on page 15.
- Design menus for the Happy and Horrible Heart restaurants. Make the chefs look healthy and not so healthy.

MFL

- Find out about special dishes of food from different countries. Go into an imaginary foreign restaurant and ask for the menu. Write simple menus in the language of the country. Learn how to ask for food and thank people.

Music

- Play different pieces of music with a clear beat. Copy the beat by clicking fingers, tapping hands or clapping. The children should add their own words as they do this. These may be nonsense at first but should develop as they repeat them. Link the words to a heartbeat and other beats that they can think of. Add instruments to the beat: percussion, and then tuned instruments. If children work in groups, they should perform to the other groups.

PE

- Discuss how our bodies are affected by exercise. Which exercises help to develop our strength by building up muscles, increase our stamina (how long we can exercise), or improve our flexibility? How can children build exercise into their lives?
- Carry out challenges to improve aspects of fitness; these could be a circuit composed of a variety of activities, each focusing on a different part of the body or a different skill. Ask questions such as: *How many times can you … in a minute? How fast/far can you …? Can you touch your toes? Does it help if you practice?*

Salt and suffer crisps

We need some salt to keep us healthy, but we should not eat too much of it. Find out why too much salt is bad for your health.

Crisps contain a lot of salt. Some of them contain far too much to be good for our health.

Look at different bags of crisps to see how much salt is in each of them. Which ones are better for you?

____

____

____

____

____

CHALLENGE

Design your own healthy crisp. You need to decide:

- ★ how many grams of crisps will be in the bag
- ★ how much salt there will be
- ★ how often you would recommend that a child should eat your crisps
- ★ what you will call the crisps
- ★ what sort of packaging the crisps will have

NOW!

Find out the amount of salt in other foods.

Make a list of foods you like to eat that have a lot of salt in them. It's not a good idea to eat too many of these!

Life Cycles

These grids demonstrate the learning objectives covered in the activities within the theme. The curriculum references indicate the relevant programme of study (PoS) for a subject area unless otherwise stated.

	Learning Objectives	**Curriculum References**
Science (Page 18)		
Scientific Enquiry	Plan and carry out an investigation into plant germination.	Sc1/2a-m
	Ask questions about plant and animal life cycles.	Sc1/2a
Life Processes and Living Things (QCA Unit 5B)	Know the life processes of reproduction in some animals and humans.	Sc2/1a
	Recognize similarities and differences between the life cycles of animals and plants.	Sc2/1c
	Know about the main stages of the human life cycle.	Sc2/2f
	Know the names of parts of the plant and their functions.	Sc2/3c
	Know and sequence the processes in a plant life cycle.	Sc2/3d
Literacy (Page 20)		
Speaking/Group Discussion and Interaction	Interview people of different ages.	En1/1a,b,c,e,f; 2a-e
	Ask questions about the origins of our fruit and vegetables.	En1/1a,b,c,e,f;2a-e
	Discuss the pros and cons of importing fruit and vegetables.	En1/3a-f
Drama	Script and act a play about the metamorphosis or life cycle of a real or imaginary animal.	En1/4a-d
Understanding and Interpreting Texts	Read and interpret the seven ages of man from Shakespeare's *As you like it.*	En2/2a-d;4a,f; En3/6a
	Find out about the life cycles of different animals and plants.	En2/3a-f
Engaging with and Responding to Texts	Evaluate stories for younger children about life cycles, such as *The very hungry caterpillar* by Eric Carle.	En2/4a-d
Creating and Shaping Texts	Write imaginary and factual texts about metamorphosis	En3/1a-e;2a-f;6a,b;7b-d
	Write a story for a younger child about a life cycle.	En3/1a-e;2a-f;9a,b,d
	Make up poems about the stages in the human life cycle.	En3/1a-e;2a-f;9a
Mathematics (Page 22)		
Using and Applying Mathematics	Use knowledge of angles to construct computer instructions to draw flower shapes.	Ma3/1b,d,e,f,g,h;2a-c;3a,b
	Look at a variety of flowers to find the number on which the stamens, petals and other parts are based.	Ma2/1a
Measuring	Measure angles.	Ma3/2a;4c
	Know that a complete rotation is 360 degrees.	Ma3/2a
Handling Data	Use a spreadsheet to compare growth and germination rates.	Ma4/1a-h;2a,b,c,f; ICT PoS 1a-c;2a,c; 4a,b,c;5a,b,c; QCA ICT Unit 5D
	Show different ways to sort a collection.	Ma4/1a,b,c,f,h;2a,c
	Collect and interpret data about fruit and vegetables for a database.	Ma4/1a-d;2a,b,c,f; ICT PoS 1a-c
	Identify mistakes in data.	Ma4/2a,b,c,f; ICT PoS 1c; QCA ICT Unit 5C

Learning Objectives	Curriculum References
Art (Page 24)	
Compare colours, shapes and textures of flowers and leaves.	PoS 1a-c;4a,b;5a,b
Observe seed cases and make some from different materials.	PoS 1a-c;2a-c;3a,b;4a,b;5a,b; QCA Art Unit 5B
Comment on the work of artists who have painted plants.	PoS 4a-c
Represent a life cycle using a range of materials.	PoS 1a-c;2a-c;3a,b;4a,b;5a,b; QCA Art Unit 5C
Make up flower patterns on the computer, using only circles.	PoS 1a-c;2a-c;3a,b;4a,b;5a,b; ICT PoS 1a,b;2b,c
Make cycles or circles, taking inspiration from artworks such as *Burning wheel* by Damien Hirst.	PoS 1a-c;2a-c;3a,b;4a,b;5a,b; ICT PoS 1a,b;2b,c;4a-c;5b
PSHCE (Page 24)	
Look at similarities and differences between humans and other living things.	PoS 1a,b;2a-f;4a,d,e,f; QCA Citizenship Unit 05
Discuss how we need to respect differences.	PoS 1a,b;2a-f;4a,d,e,f; QCA Citizenship Unit 05
Design & Technology (Page 24)	
Make models of fruit using different materials.	PoS 1a-d;2a-e;3a-c;4a,b;5b
Make spinning seeds.	PoS 1a-d;2a-e;3a-c;4a,b;5b
Geography (Page 26)	
Identify where our fruit and vegetables come from.	PoS 2c
Compare the lives of children around the world.	PoS 1b,c,e;2a,c,d,f;3a-g;4a;5b; QCA Citizenship Unit 05
History (Page 26)	
Undertake a potato survey – naming varieties, properties, when they were introduced to the country, and where they came from.	PoS 1a,b;2a-d;4a;5a; ICT PoS 1a-c; 5a; QCA History Unit 19
PE (Page 26)	
Make individual or group symmetrical movements to depict life cycles.	PoS 1a,b;2a-c;3a,b; QCA PE Unit 27
Repeat movements to make up a cycle.	PoS 1a,b;2a-c;3a,b; QCA PE Unit 27
Music (Page 26)	
Devise repeated sounds with a range of timings and using different instruments.	PoS 2a,b;3a-c;5a-c
Use patterns in sound to represent a life cycle.	PoS 2a,b;3a-c;5a-c

Science

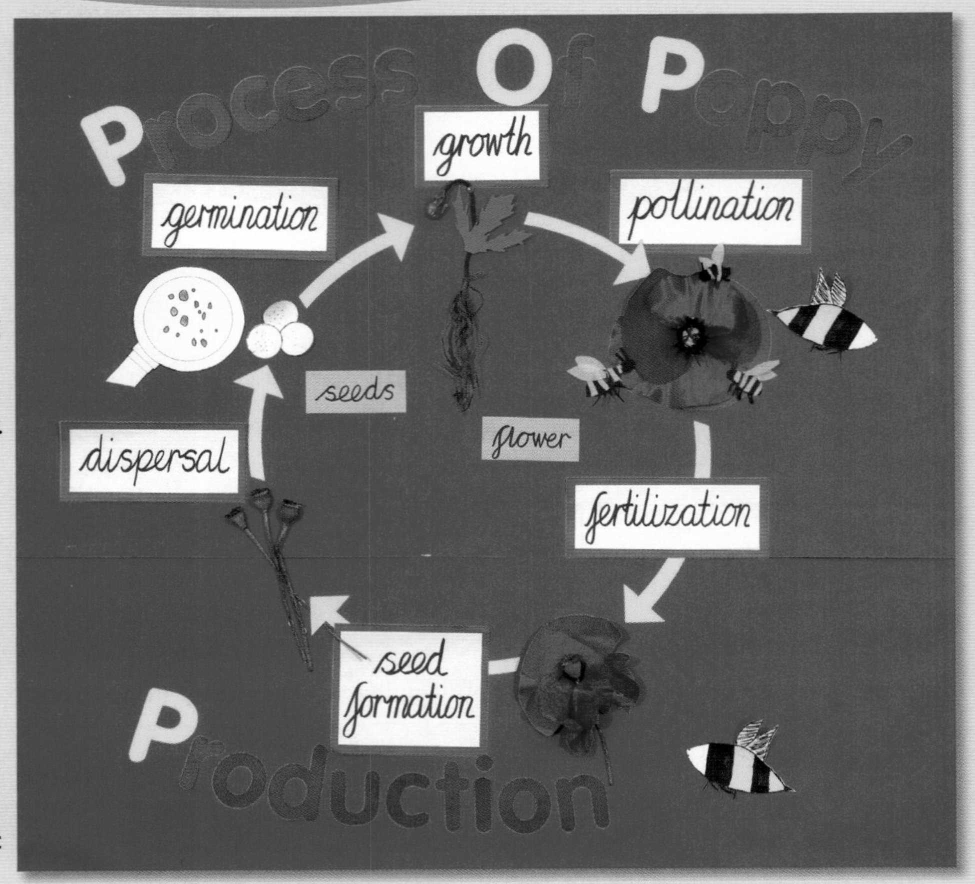

Starting Points

- Provide plants for the children to explore and identify parts – include leaves, roots, stem, flowers and fruit if possible. Plants should be simple flowering plants, cultivated or wild with symmetrical flowers – rose, tulip, buttercup, apple, celandine, poppy. Flowers such as dandelion or daffodil are not so appropriate as they either have flowers consisting of florets or are not symmetrical. Draw observations of different parts of the flower (not the rest of the plant) and label parts with name and function.
- Put the stages of a plant life cycle in order as shown on the display. Discuss meanings of the scientific terms for the different stages.

Enquiry

- Investigate one stage of the life cycle, such as the germination rate. Discuss what seeds need in order to germinate (all seeds need water, oxygen and a suitable temperature; some germinate better in light conditions and some in dark). Predict how much water the seeds need. Set up an experiment to discover the optimum amount.

  Decide together:

  - What seeds to use (beans, peas, mustard and cress or flower seeds are all appropriate).
  - How many to test? What happens if one fails to germinate?
  - How much water will be given and how often.
  - Factors that should be kept the same to make a valid comparison.
  - What data will be kept, by whom and in what format When did the first shoot appear? What happened next? Did all of them grow? Discuss the importance of keeping a control.
  - At the end, make a generalisation about the amount of water that is best for the germination of those seeds.

Extension Activities

- Discuss the purpose of a life cycle. If there were no cycle, the plant or animal would die out.
- Investigate different methods of seed dispersal. Evaluate why each method is useful to the plant. Carry out an investigation into one method – for example, how long it takes a winged seed to fall, or how far seeds land away from the parent plant. See the activity sheet on page 19.
- Grow some fruit and vegetables, giving each what they need to grow well. Compare growth after a time and discuss how growth could be improved. Take home the produce!
- Trace the life cycles of some familiar animals and match similar stages with a plant that's been studied. Include the human life cycle. Put stages in order. Compare the life cycles of plants and animals.

Ed's quiz

Under each seed above write the name of the plant it comes from (from the list on the left), and A,B,C,D, E or F to show how it is dispersed, using the clues below.

Ed's clues!

A Some fruits with seeds inside are eaten by birds. The seeds are later dropped in a new place.

B Some seeds have wings or are very light and are carried by the wind.

C Some plants have seeds in a type of pepper pot that shakes in the wind and makes the seeds fly out.

D Some seeds are heavy but still float and are carried away by water.

E Some seeds grip onto animal fur and later drop off.

F Some seed pods violently throw seeds into the air when the seed pod dries and breaks open.

NOW!

Collect some of your own seeds and say how you think they are dispersed.

Literacy

Speaking and Listening

- Act out the life cycle of an imaginary or real animal or plant.
- Ask questions about where our fruit and vegetables come from. Discuss why we import food and debate if this is a good or bad thing. Link with geography.

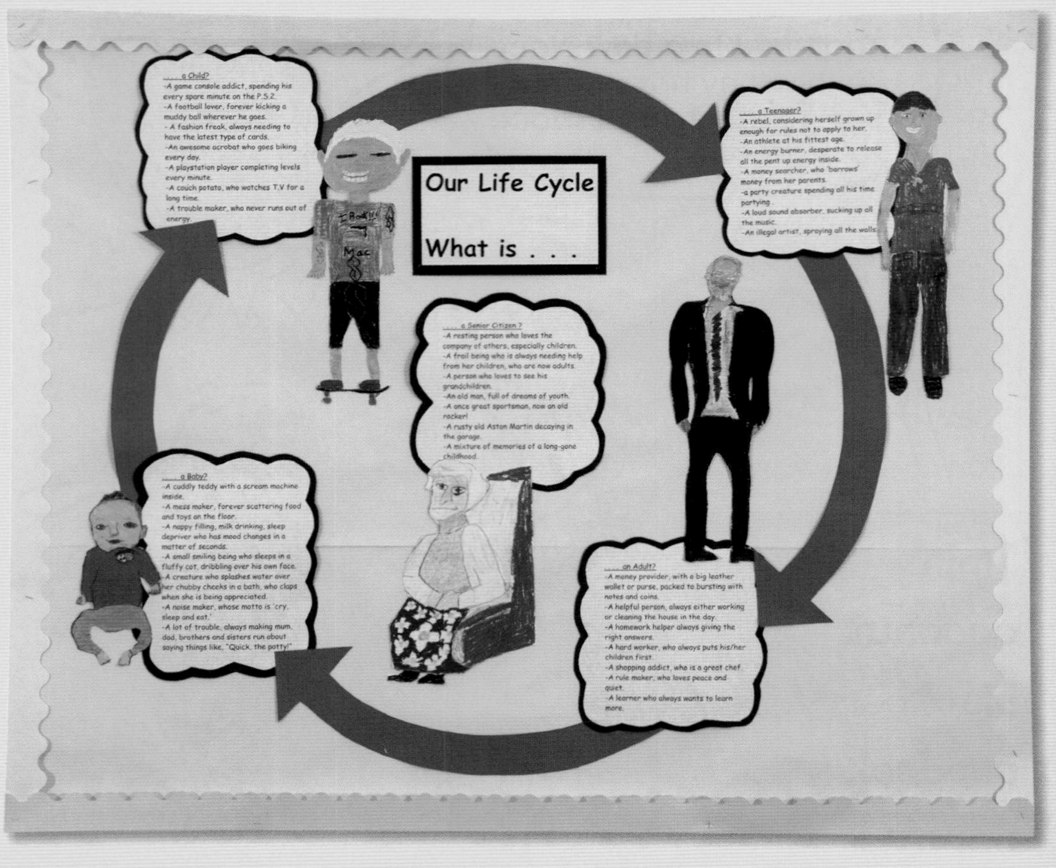

Reading and Writing

- Read 'The seven ages of man' from William Shakespeare's *As you Like it*. There are many references that can be investigated at www.phrases.org.uk/meanings. The children will not understand many of the words, but after several readings ask them to identify the number and names of ages he lists in human life and the basic characteristics of each age. Find out the meanings of words in the text of which they are unsure (pantaloon, pard, sans). Today, the ages will be different. Children should be modern day Shakespeares and decide on their own 7 stages of human life, which could be: *Baby; Toddler; Child; Teenager; Parent; Grandparent; Elderly person.*

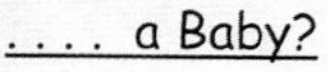

. . . . a Baby?
-A cuddly teddy with a scream machine inside.
-A mess maker, forever scattering food and toys on the floor.
-A nappy filling, milk drinking, sleep depriver who has mood changes in a matter of seconds.
-A small smiling being who sleeps in a fluffy cot, dribbling over his own face.
-A creature who splashes water over her chubby cheeks in a bath, who claps when she is being appreciated.
-A noise maker, whose motto is 'cry, sleep and eat.'
-A lot of trouble, always making mum, dad, brothers and sisters run about saying things like, "Quick, the potty!"

- Discuss the characteristics of different ages. Children should observe or interview people from the different ages. Invite visitors to school – a mother and child, a grandparent, a teenager and so on.
- Ask the children to describe a life cycle that involves metamorphosis, such as a butterfly or frog. Compose poems called 'Metamorphosis'; each verse should show stages of change, feelings or appearance. Write and illustrate as a cycle, as in the display above.
- Read *The very hungry caterpillar* by Eric Carle (Puffin Books, 1994). Consider its style and presentation for a younger child. Devise a story about another animal and decide how to present it.
- A plant goes through different stages of growth in its life cycle. Investigate these on the activity sheet on page 21.

Life cycles

Marlin lives in the town. He has come to the country for a holiday. He is amazed at all the different types of plants around. He loves the yellow fields of buttercups. His friend Jo tries to explain about buttercups and how they grow each year to make the fields so yellow. The table shows what she said. What do you think of her definitions? Could you do better?

Make up your own definition, using the words to help you.

Words to help you:

root	water	seed	energy	conditions
flower	stigma	pollen	stamen	ovum

Process	Jo's definition	My definition
Germinate	Starts to grow	

Process	Jo's definition	My definition
Grow	Gets bigger	

Process	Jo's definition	My definition
Pollinate	Bees come	

Process	Jo's definition	My definition
Fertilise	It makes seed	

Process	Jo's definition	My definition
Disperse	Seeds go away	

Maths

Using and Applying

- Create flower patterns, like those displayed on this page, using an ICT programme. For ideas see: *Superlogo Challenge* at www.kented.org.uk/ngfl/ict/teaching/documents/logo-handout.doc.

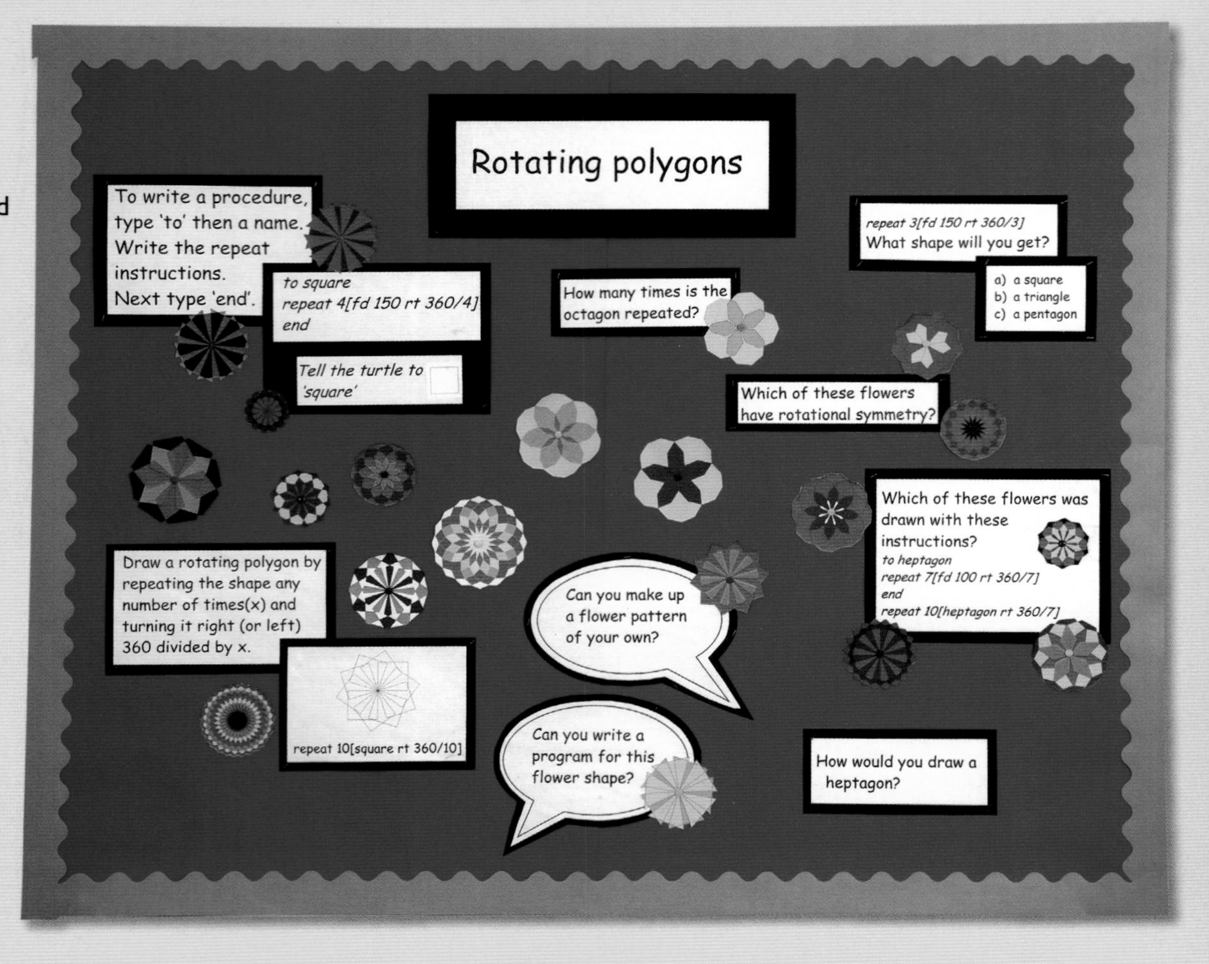

Handling Data

- Provide a database for the children with details of plant growth that are correct, but which also has data that has mistakes in it for them to detect and correct. Put both sets (uncorrected and corrected) on a line graph to show how graphs can show up mistakes more easily than tables or numbers alone.
- Collect and store information about plant parts and growth. Challenge children to put in some implausible information for others to detect as on the activity sheet on page 23.
- Building on past experiences of sorting, think of as many ways as possible to sort a collection of fruit and vegetables – for example Venn diagrams, or Carroll diagrams for two characteristics which may be suggested by the children, for example:

A Carroll Diagram

	green	**not green**
contains seeds	cucumber courgette	red pepper tomato
does not contain seeds	lettuce broccoli brussell sprout	potato onion parsnip celery

The children could try creating a Carroll diagram with fruits, or a collection of leaves or flowers which would need other pairs of characteristics. It is always best for children to examine real fruit and vegetables when doing this activity.

How much water?

Put the following data onto a line graph:

Rajid gave the seeds 10 ml of water each day.

	Length of stem	Number of leaves	Appearance
Day 1	No stem	No leaves	Root started growing
Day 3	2cm	2	Root long
Day 5	4.5cm	5	Stem and leaves green
Day 7	6cm	3	Healthy, strong stem
Day 9	9cm	10	Healthy and green

Karen gave the seeds 20ml of water each day.

	Length of stem	Number of leaves	Appearance
Day 1	No stem	No leaves	Root growing
Day 3	2cm	2	Stem green
Day 5	4.5cm	3	Leaves green
Day 7	4cm	4	Stem turning brown
Day 9	9cm	7	Stem collapsing

Peter gave the seeds 30ml of water each day.

	Length of stem	Number of leaves	Appearance
Day 1	No stem	No leaves	Root starting to grow
Day 3	2cm	2	Stem brown
Day 5	2.5cm	3	All going slimy
Day 7	2cm	3	Water lying on surface
Day 9	1cm	3	Plant rotting

What do the results show?

There are mistakes in this data. Can you find them? Change the data to make sense.

Can you find other ways to show these results?

Try this investigation yourself to find out if the results are real or not.

Art

- Explore the textures, colours, shapes and patterns of real flowers, leaves and seed cases. Look critically at pictures by artists such as Pierre-Auguste Renoir (1841–1919), Claude Monet (1840–1926), Vincent Van Gogh (1853–1890), Georgia O'Keefe (1887–1986) and Gustav Klimt (1862–1918), all of whom painted poppies. Choose other types of flowers, and make a work of art like the one on this page. Select materials such as watercolour, oil paints, pastels, collage, crayons, textiles or stitching to make a display as shown below.
- Look at seeds that grow in a pod. How are they kept safe? What textures are there? Select fabrics to best represent each part of a pod, and combine to make a pod picture. It could be abstract, using only the textures, or a still life. Other media, such as paints, could be added for effect.
- Ask the children to make a 3-D pod for an imaginary seed. Select shape, texture and materials. What will the seed look like? What does it need to grow?
- Experiment making your own cycle designs. Look at 'Burning wheel' from *In a spin, the action of the world on things* by Damien Hirst (b. 1965): see the image at www.collection.britishcouncil.org. Make an electrical spinner as described on the activity sheet on page 25 and create 'in a spin' designs.

PSHCE

- Discuss how all living things are similar in many ways but have some differences. Look at physical similarities between children in the class before differences. Make a class picture of hands and colour them as a background. On top, write all the similarities between them and then the differences. Think of differences other than appearance – culture, way of life, beliefs. Join hands to show respect and care for each other as a start to considering our values and beliefs.

Design & Technology

- Make up a class fruit bowl. Create fruit from papier mâché, clay or modroc. Ensure that the texture, colour and shininess of fruits are copied as well as the shape and size. Evaluate the results.
- Collect a variety of seeds that spin as they are dispersed – sycamore, ash, lime. Make your own versions using appropriate materials.

Spinning colour

You can make your own spinning pattern.

First make an electrical spinner.

You will need:

- A plastic tub
- An electric circuit with battery, wires and a motor
- A cog to attach to the spindle of the motor
- Pieces of plain card
- Paint

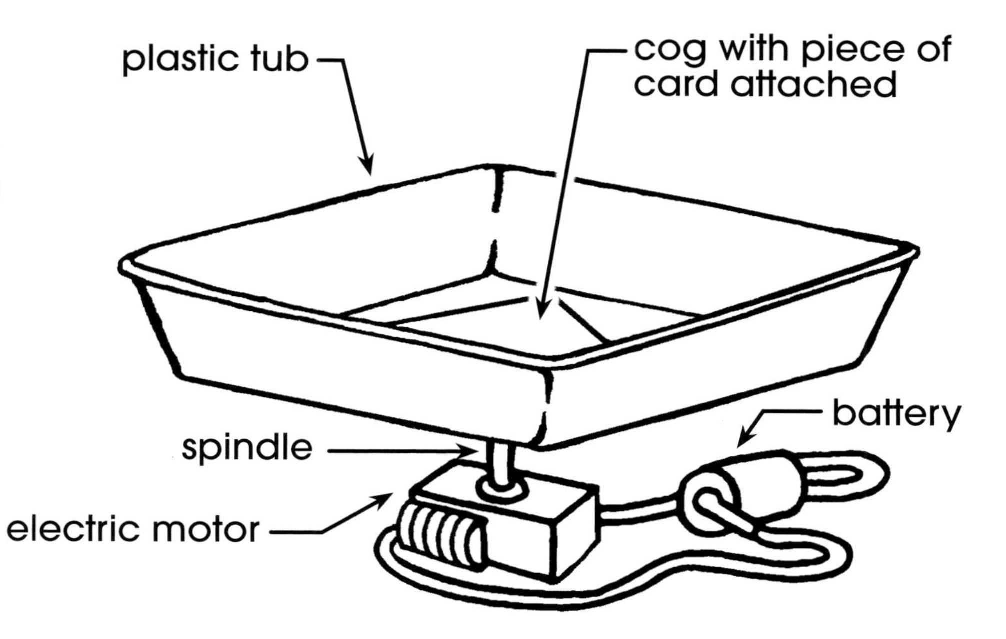

This is what you do!

1. Make a hole on the underside of the plastic tub, near the centre.
2. Attach the circuit to the plastic tub so that the spindle of the motor pokes through the hole.
3. Put a piece of card on the spindle inside the plastic tub so that it can spin round freely.
4. Whilst spinning the card, slowly drip a little paint onto the surface. Look at the pattern made. Add more paint or another colour, gradually building up a pattern.

Geography

- Identify where fruit and vegetables in our supermarkets are grown and how they get to our country. Consider issues such as the distance travelled and effect on the environment. Ask questions about them – why they are imported? Are any exported? See the display for more ideas

History

- Look at a variety of potatoes; investigate their life cycle and their names. Discuss how often we eat them and the different ways in which they can be cooked. Find out about the introduction of potatoes to England in Tudor times by Sir Walter Raleigh (c. 1552–1618). Discuss the food value of them. If the skins are eaten, potatoes contain many of the essential vitamins that we need, as well as fibre. Potatoes cooked without a lot of fat are good for our health. Find out when other fruit and vegetables were introduced to the country.

PE

- Act out the change in a plant throughout its life cycle, accompanied by sounds – bursting through the seed coating, slowly growing, waving in the breeze, bees visiting, seeds dispersing, and growing again.
- Make up a routine of repeated movements, as in a life cycle.

Music

- Make up a round to sing that describes a plant's life cycle. Use a common tune for the round – see the activity sheet on page 27 for an example to help children to remember the order of events in the cycle and the plant parts involved. Once they have mastered this, ask groups to devise verses using a familiar round or tune for the life cycle of any animal, including humans.

Life cycle song

Here are some verses to help you remember what happens in a plant life cycle.

Practise these verses to the tune of Frère Jacques:

1. Li-ife cycle × 2
Round and round × 2
Se-ed grows to pla-ant
Pla-ant ma-akes se-eds
Round and round × 2

2. Germination × 2
Ro-ots grow × 2
Taking i-in wa-ter × 2
Helps it grow × 2

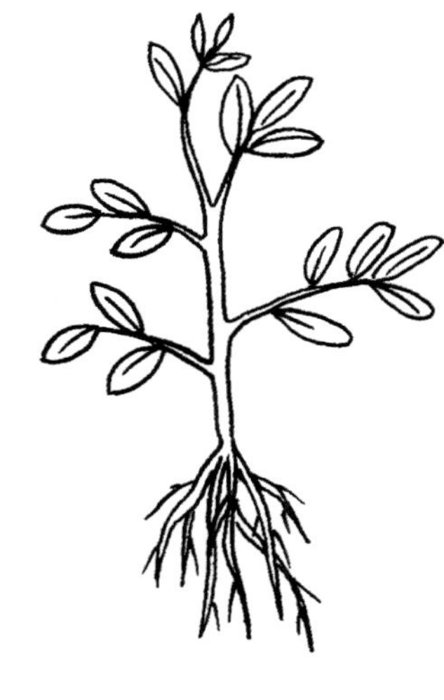

3. Growing bigger × 2
Stems and leaves × 2
Mixing air and water
I-in th-e sunlight
To make food × 2

4. Pollination × 2
Insects come × 2
Take pollen from the stamens
Leave it on the stigma
In the flower × 2

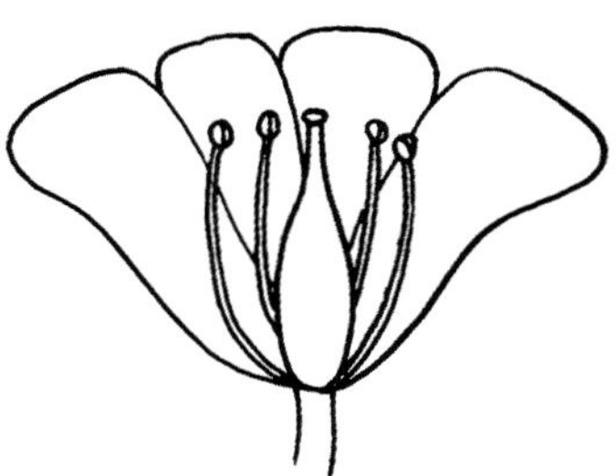

5. Fertilisation × 2
Pollen travels × 2
Do-wn th-e sty-le
Joi-ns with the ovule
Makes a seed × 2

6. Di-spersal × 2
Seeds are spread × 2
By water, air, explosion,
Or animals and bi-rds
To new ground × 2

'–' shows you where to put extra syllables into the words to make them fit the tune. You may be able to think of better words.

NOW! **Choose another tune and make up verses for an animal life cycle.**

Changing State

These grids demonstrate the learning objectives covered in the activities within the theme. The curriculum references indicate the relevant programme of study (PoS) for a subject area unless otherwise stated.

	Learning Objectives	Curriculum References
Science (Page 30)		
Scientific Enquiry	Use measuring equipment for temperature, including sensors, accurately.	Sc1/2e,f
	Monitor rainfall over a period of time.	Sc1/2e,f
	Investigate melting rates.	Sc1/1b;2a-m
Materials and their Properties (QCA Science Unit 5D)	Sort materials into solids, liquids and gases.	Sc3/1e
	Name processes that cause materials to change.	Sc3/2a,b,d,g
	Identify processes in the water cycle.	Sc3/2e
	Know that temperature measures how hot a material is.	Sc3/2c
Literacy (Page 32)		
Speaking	Discuss recent and historical disasters to do with tsunamis, floods, drought etc.	En1/1a-f;2a-e
	Act out a scripted play about one of the changes studied.	En1/4a-d
	Represent the water cycle through drama.	En1/4a-d
	Act feelings of hot and cold.	En1/4a-d
Understanding and Interpreting Texts	Read books or newspapers to find out about water-related disasters in the world.	En2/2c,d;3a-g;9a-c
Engaging with and Responding to Texts	Read poems and stories that depict changing state, and comment on them.	En2/2a-d;3a-f
Creating and Shaping Texts	Script a play/make a booklet about freezing or other changes.	En3/1a-e;9a-d
	Make booklets about water and its forms.	En3/1a-e;2a-f;12
Maths (Page 34)		
Measuring	Select the right thermometers to measure given temperatures.	Ma2/1c;Sc1/2e-g; ICT PoS 5b
	Measure volume, circumference and temperature accurately.	Ma3/1a,g;4a,b
	Measure circumferences of ice balloons.	Ma2/1c; Ma3/4e
Handling Data	Make and interpret bar graphs and line graphs about temperature change.	Ma4/1a,c,d,e,f,g;2a-f
	Calculate the average and the range of temperatures.	Ma4/1a;2d; Sc1/1b;2e,f

Learning Objectives	Curriculum References
Design & Technology (Page 36)	
Make umbrellas.	PoS 1a-d;2a-e;3a-c; ICT PoS 2b,c;5b
Art (Page 36)	
Make water designs for fabrics or pictures	PoS 1a;2a-c;4a,b;5a-c; QCA Art Unit 5A
Compare paintings of umbrellas by Claude Monet and Pierre-Auguste Renoir	PoS 4c
Make marbled covers for books about water and how it changes	PoS 2b,c;4b
PE (Page 36)	
Represent weather conditions in group movement	PoS 1a,b;2a;3a,b
Music (Page 36)	
Listen and respond to different genres of water music	PoS 4a-d
Make up accompaniments to own poems about changes in water	PoS 2a,b
PSHCE (Page 38)	
Learn about water disasters in the world and their effect on the environment and people	PoS 2a,j;4b
Devise a poster to show ways of saving water	PoS 1a,c;2a,d,f,j;5e; En3/5a,b;7a-d;9a-d
Geography (Page 38)	
Identify areas in the world that have different temperatures and amounts of water	PoS 2a,c,d,f;3a-g; QCA Geography Unit 11
Find out about the life of a child in a country that has little rainfall	PoS 3a-d; QCA Geography Unit 11
Understand components of the water cycle	PoS 4a,b; QCA Geography Unit 14 PSHCE PoS 4e: QCA PSHCE Unit 05
Understand the part rivers play in changing the landscape	PoS 3a-g;4a,b;5a,b; QCA Geography Unit 14
History (Page 38)	
Find out about diseases carried by water in the past – typhoid, dysentery	PoS 2a-c;4a;5b,c
Find out how these diseases were treated	PoS 2a-c;4a;5b,c
Compare health treatment now and in Victorian times	PoS 2a-c;4a;5b,c; QCA History Unit 12

Science

Starting Points

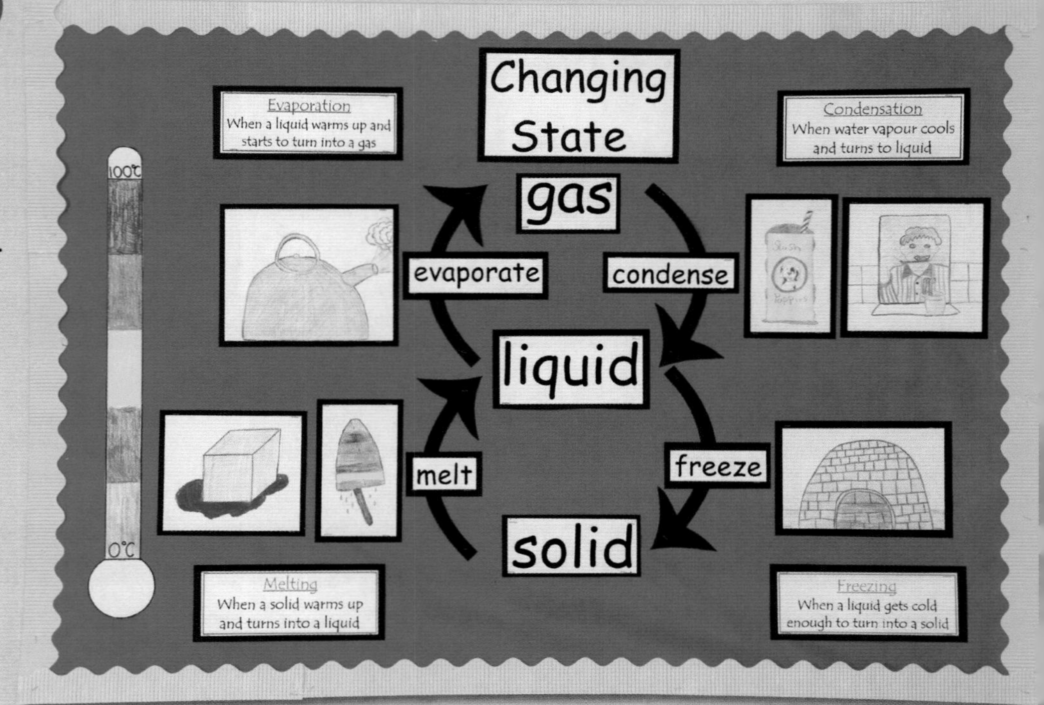

- Provide cards with names of changes, and ask the children to match changes to pictures or actual objects. For example:
  - a block of ice melting;
  - water condensing on the outside of a very cold drinks can;
  - cold salt water in a bowl left for some time to show how the level has gone down. Colour water to make it clear that the level has changed (evaporation);
  - a lolly freezing.
- Compare boiling and evaporation – when does each occur? What are the similarities and differences?
- Write the changes as arrow diagrams, for example: Ice $\xrightarrow{\text{heat}}$ water $\xrightarrow{\text{heat}}$ water vapour (steam)

  solid   liquid   gas

Enquiry

- Try investigating the freezing rates of different volumes of water, or different concentrations of salt water.
- Encourage the children to predict, hypothesise and make decisions about how to test, record, interpret and evaluate results.
- To find a pattern, they need to change one factor and test at least three different volumes or concentrations.
- Relate the results to real life situations by comparing the rate of freezing of fresh water and salt water puddles. Hypothesise whether still or moving water would freeze more quickly.

Extension Activities

- Compare freezing rates of different liquids – milk, fruit juice, vinegar, washing up liquid and others suggested by children. Do not include oily liquids as they will not freeze in an ordinary freezer – their freezing points are too low.
- Complete the activity sheet on page 31. Here is a suggested order for the explanations on the sheet:

Jane	3	Links results to original prediction. No scientific vocabulary.
Sajid	4	Correct idea but only an observation, no explanation. Linked to the test.
Philip	6	No link to the test.
Jack	1	Uses scientific vocabulary (evaporation); links results to the test
Joss	8	Incorrect science, not about dissolving.
Richard	2	Links results to the test; correct idea; no use of scientific vocabulary.
Sally	5	No link to the test. Correct idea.
Pat	8	Incorrect science.

None of these explanations is perfect. Discuss with children the good and bad points of each. It is essential to link their results to an explanation, to get the science right and to use scientific vocabulary if appropriate.

The cat's water problem

The cat's water bowl always seemed to be empty. Tom the cat could not possibly drink so much each day.

Children in a class decided that the water must have evaporated. They tested this idea.

Some children looked at the results and explained **WHY** it happened. Read the explanations. Who has the best idea? Rate their ideas.

Name	Explanation	Rating 1= best 8 = worst
Jane	Water disappeared quickly in the big dish. It went up into the air quicker.	
Sajid	In the big dish it went away quicker.	
Philip	It's all about evaporation. When something evaporates it changes from a liquid into a gas and rises up into the air.	
Jack	The evaporation was quicker from a large surface because there is more surface for the air to get to the water.	
Joss	It was about evaporation and dissolving. More water could dissolve into the air from the big container.	
Richard	The greater the surface area the more water rises up into the air.	
Sally	Water was in contact with the air. The air made it change into steam. We couldn't see it but it was still happening.	
Pat	The bigger the area the more air was touching the water and air makes it dissolve and then evaporate. It goes up into the air more easily.	

Is your order different from your friend's?

Do any of the children have wrong ideas about evaporation?

Write your own explanation.

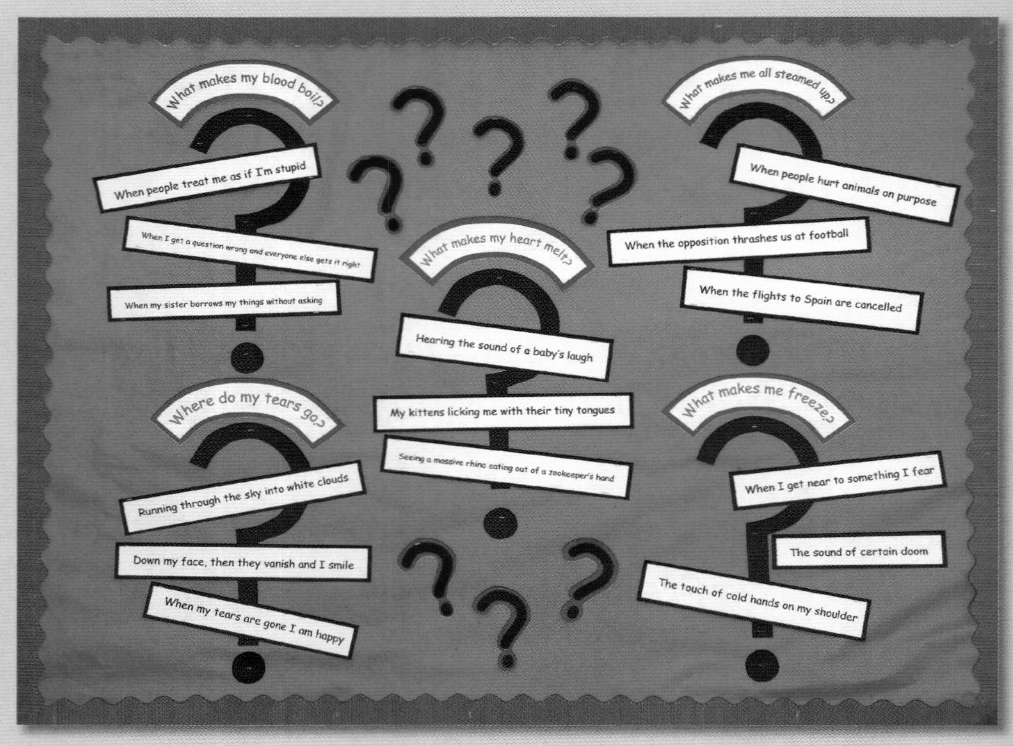

Literacy

Reading and Writing

- Show the children a question about an aspect of change they have studied. Provide them with a strip of paper to write their own imaginative response to it.

  For example:
  - What makes my heart melt?
  - The feel of a kitten's fur on my face.

  Or sit in pairs with one child asking a question and the other responding. Change over. The display shows the variety of responses from children.
- Introduce other questions about all sorts of changes and make up a change poem, or use the activity sheet on the following page.
- Give children words that represent hot or cold feelings. They make a list of words and phrases to describe the word for others to guess – for example **freezing**: shiver, red nose, breath shows like steam; **boiling**: bubbles, bubbling surface, invisible gas, sweat, red face, flushed.

  Use these to compose changing state poems, which could be haiku:

  Burning:
  It's so hot I burn
  Crumble into grey powder
  Now changed forever.

  Evaporating:
  No rain, hot, hot Sun
  Red face, sweat runs down in streams
  Now gone. That's better!

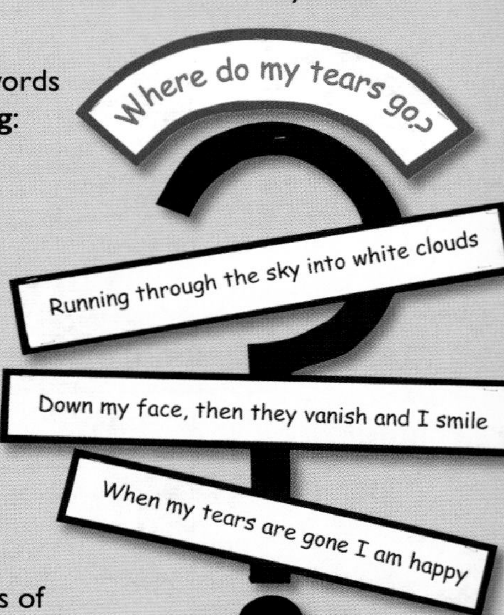

- Alternatively, develop into descriptive writing – create the opening paragraphs of an adventure or mystery story, or make up headlines for a newspaper report.
- Ask the children to make up questions about ice or fire. Write these on strips of paper and sort into those that can be answered by doing and those that need a secondary source to find the answer.
- Read 'The Water Cycle' by Roger Stevens from the book *Why otters don't wear socks* (Macmillan). Read other poems on a similar theme. Comment on them – why are some liked more than others? Use to stimulate questions and to trace the life of other liquids: for example, 'Milk on my cereal' or 'Tomato ketchup'.
- Ask the children to make up a water booklet with at least three chapters to illustrate different aspects of change. This could be a group booklet with different chapters by different people.

Speaking and Listening

- Ask the children to devise and script a play about the changes studied – fiction or narrative – suggested titles could be 'The frost fiend' or 'London's burning'.
- Organize a water festival to share with others. This could be truly cross-curricular as water is essential to every living thing; it has uses in sport, art, and other activities, and many nations have customs about it. Choose a particular date of significance – for example the anniversary of a sea battle, a food disaster or the building of the school pond.

Feelings

All these questions need a one line answer.

After each one decide what feeling it is about.

Then write a one line answer to the question. Be as imaginative as you can and choose words carefully. Remember! You only have one line for each answer.

What makes my heart melt? *Feeling:* ____________________

My answer: ____

What makes my blood boil? *Feeling:* ____________________

My answer: ____

What makes me freeze? *Feeling:* ____________________

My answer: ____

What makes my fear evaporate? *Feeling:* ____________________

My answer: ____

Now write out the questions and answers as a poem.

Read it to your teacher or a friend.

NOW!

Think of some more questions like this and ask a friend to answer them.

Maths

Measuring

- Make some ice balloons
  - Place the nozzle of a balloon over a tap, support the balloon at the bottom with a hand and fill with water. Tie a knot, place in a plastic bag and keep in a freezer for 2 days.
  - Record how the balloon changes over time. Use the activity sheet on page 35 to record the results.
  - Frozen balloons will have a larger circumference because water expands on freezing. Investigate this further as follows: fill film canisters with water, replace the lids, and freeze. When frozen, the lids will be pushed up by the ice.

SAFETY!
BE CAREFUL WHEN CUTTING PLASTIC

- Make a rain gauge to measure rainfall, by cutting open a large plastic bottle, inverting the top and fixing it over the bottle to act as a funnel. Place it in the ground outside and measure the volume of rainfall by tipping collected rainwater into a measuring cylinder. Children could suggest how to calibrate their rain gauges. Find average rainfall over a period of time for the area and compare with the rest of the country.

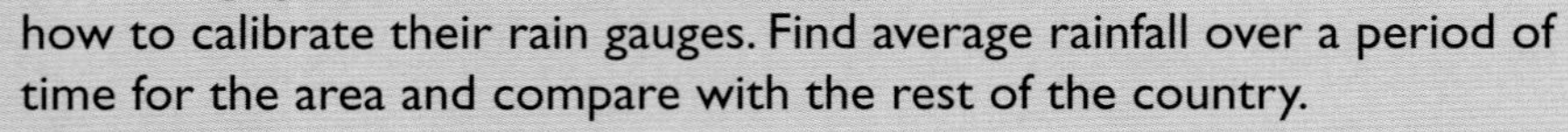

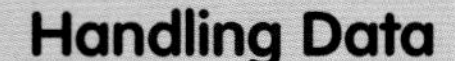

Handling Data

- Investigate the melting rates of ice pops placed in different locations around the school. Record the results in a table and convert the data to graphs as on the display.
- Show the children a line graph of a changing temperature in a particular place. Ask them to talk about when it increases and decreases. Give them ideas of what might have happened to cause variations, for example: it went up quickly because a fire broke out in the classroom, or someone put a strong light next to the thermometer.

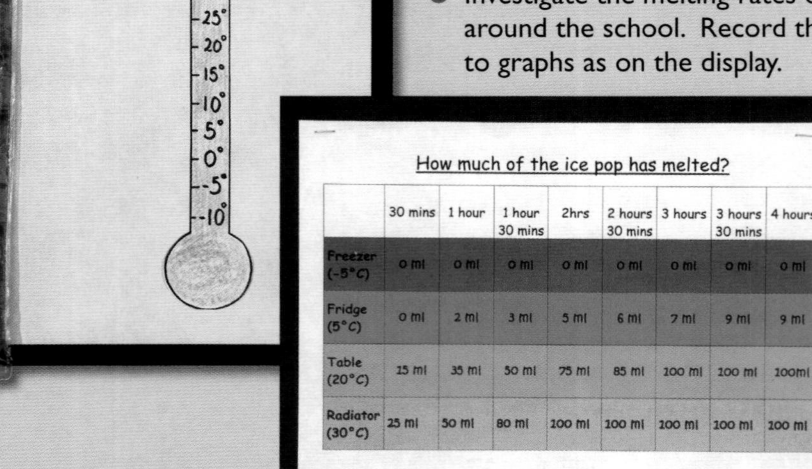

How much of the ice pop has melted?

	30 mins	1 hour	1 hour 30 mins	2hrs	2 hours 30 mins	3 hours	3 hours 30 mins	4 hours
Freezer (-5°C)	0 ml	0 ml	0 ml	0 ml	0 ml	0 ml	0 ml	0 ml
Fridge (5°C)	0 ml	2 ml	3 ml	5 ml	6 ml	7 ml	9 ml	9 ml
Table (20°C)	15 ml	35 ml	50 ml	75 ml	85 ml	100 ml	100 ml	100ml
Radiator (30°C)	25 ml	50 ml	80 ml	100 ml	100 ml	100 ml	100 ml	100 ml

Our ice balloons

You will need three ice balloons in this enquiry. You will be measuring size and time.

Write instructions showing how to make an ice balloon.

Information about our ice balloons

Questions	Measurements		
What is the circumference before freezing?	Balloon 1	Balloon 2	Balloon 3
What is the circumference after freezing?	Balloon 1	Balloon 2	Balloon 3
What is the temperature of each balloon?	Before freezing 1. 2. 3.	After freezing 1. 2. 3.	
How long do they take to melt?	In water 1. 2. 3.	In the room 1. 2. 3.	In the fridge 1. 2. 3.

Look at the data you have collected about your ice balloons. Which things surprised you?

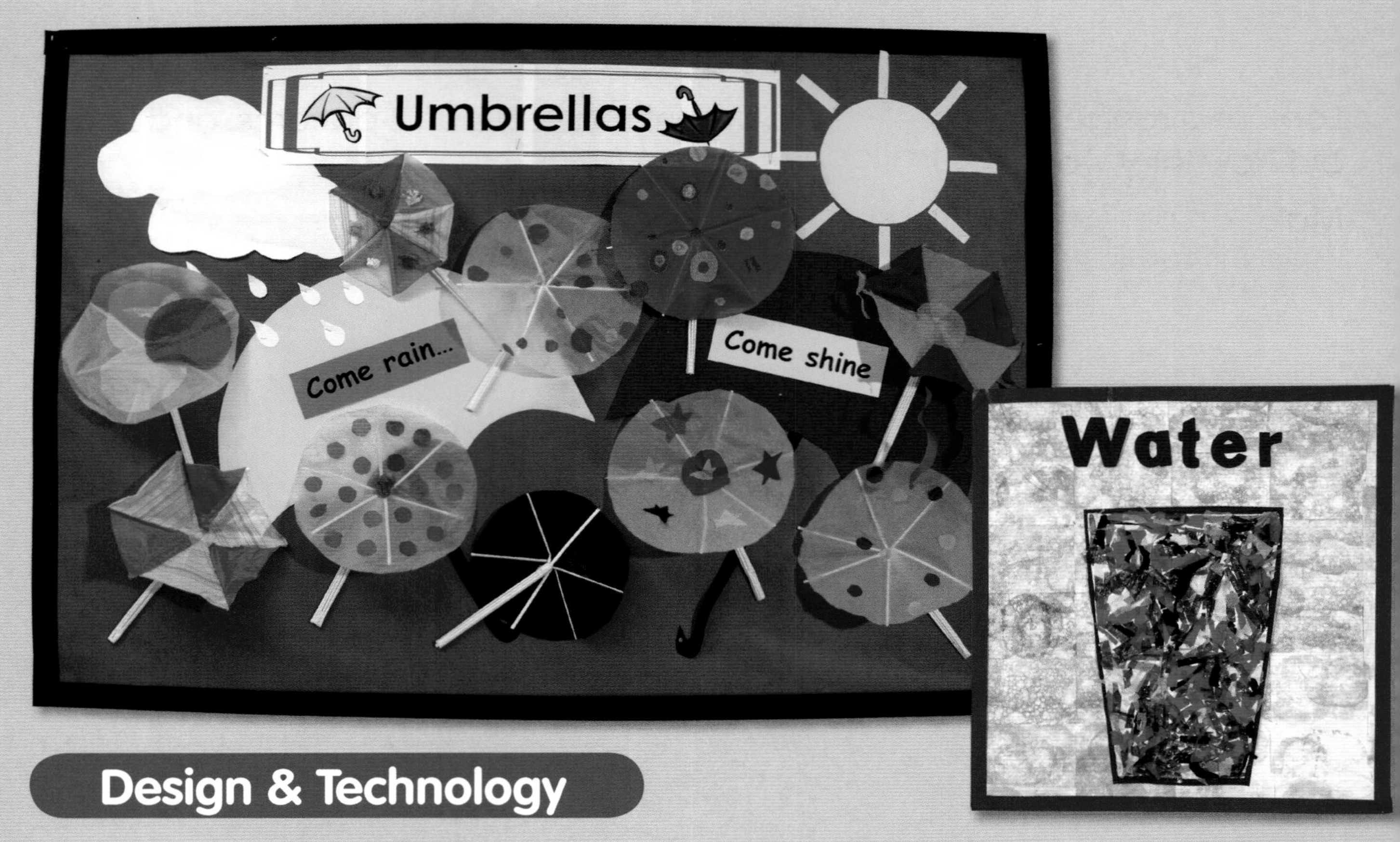

Design & Technology

- Look at a range of different umbrellas – children's umbrellas, golf umbrellas, or tiny ones for drinks. Look at the mechanism to keep the umbrella up. Can children devise ways to make theirs raise and lower? See the activity sheet on page 37 to make umbrellas like those on the display above.

Art

- Compare paintings of umbrellas by Claude Monet (1842–1926) and Pierre-Auguste Renoir (1841–1919). Which style do children prefer and why? Copy pictures and cut up into six regular pieces that tessellate, such as squares or rectangles. Ask six different children to copy one piece each and put together again to make their own Monet or Renoir.
- Look at water and make up colours for it. Drop things in it, or swirl it with a stick to make patterns. Create artwork based on what is seen – a description in colour and pattern, like the display above, right.
- Make marbled covers for books about water and how it changes from one state to another.

PE

- Ask the children to imagine being in certain weather conditions – a hot desert, the Arctic, or in a thunderstorm. Move in different ways to represent the conditions and how they change. Combine with music to compose a dance.

Music

- Listen to music about water and its forms; classical music such as *The raindrop* by Frederic Chopin (1810–1849), *Swirl* by Todd Levin (b. 1971), *La mer* by Claude Debussy (1862–1918), *Sea symphony* by Ralph Vaughan Williams (1872–1958); traditional folk songs such as *Haul Away Boys* and *Rio Grande*. Also include any popular music that is appropriate. Discuss how any particular piece makes children feel and what they like and dislike about it. What rhythms are there? Can they copy them? Can they identify instruments playing in selected parts? Use this to stimulate artwork.
- Devise accompaniments to the children's own poems, using instruments alongside different materials for sound effects. Repeat, showing clearly changes from one state to another – water melting, freezing, boiling, condensing or evaporating.

Keep the rain out!

Look at a range of umbrellas in different materials and patterns, and find out how they work.

Make an umbrella framework from paper art straws like this:

PSHCE

- Ask the children to read and listen to current news. Indicate problems in the world concerned with climate change and its results, such as drought, floods, alterations to the ice caps and the effect on people there.
- Ask the children to find out about the life of a child in a country with little rain, or one with too much rain.
- Make posters to show ways of saving water.

Geography

- Note places around the school where water collects. Record changes in puddles and discuss where the water goes. Link this to the whole water cycle.
- Study the position and features of local rivers/streams/ponds. Locate on a map. Look at the great rivers of the world and identify them on world maps and globes. Find out how water affects the landscape through erosion and other processes – see the display.
- Identify areas in the world that have high/low temperatures all year or high/low rainfall all year. Find countries that have combinations of these – high rainfall and temperatures, low temperatures and high rainfall, and so on. The children could try to find patterns in areas with similar conditions.

History

- Find out about diseases carried by water in the past, such as typhoid and dysentery. Find out how they were treated then and how they are treated now. Where in the world are these diseases now most common and why?
- Research the work of John Snow (1813–1858), a Victorian scientist who believed that cholera was transmitted by dirty water. See the activity sheet on page 39.

spray

The Man who Helped the Health of Londoners

23rd June 1854

Today, the famous scientist, John Snow, announced his amazing theory!

Many of the people living in Soho, a poor part of London, have been dying of the dreadful disease, cholera. Now they have hope that the spread of the disease will be stopped if John Snow is correct.

Find out about the work of John Snow. There are clues in the beginning of this newspaper article about one of his important discoveries. Finish the article.

Earth, Sun and Moon

These grids demonstrate the learning objectives covered in the activities within the theme. The curriculum references indicate the relevant programme of study (PoS) for a subject area unless otherwise stated.

	Learning Objectives	Curriculum References
Science (Page 42)		
Scientific Enquiry (QCA unit 5E)	Carry out an investigation into how shadows change during the day.	Sc1/2b,d-j
	Find out how day and night are formed.	Sc1/1a
	Explain how the tilt of the Earth and its orbit round the Sun causes the seasons in the different hemispheres.	Sc1/1a
	Show why we see different shapes of the Moon.	Sc1/1a
Physical Processes	Link ideas about the solar system.	Sc4/4c,d
	Know the shape and relative sizes of the Earth, Sun and Moon.	Sc4/4a
	Know how shadows change during the day and year.	Sc4/4b
	Know how relative movements of the Earth, Sun and Moon inform units of time.	Sc4/4c,d
	Understand why we always see the same side of the Moon.	Sc4/4d
Literacy (Page 44)		
Speaking	Interview a child in a role as an astronaut.	En1/1a,b,e
Listening and Responding/ Group Interaction and Discussion	Debate the importance of space exploration.	En1/a-f;2a-e;3a-f
Understanding and Interpreting Texts	Research space travel.	En2/3a-e
	Find facts about the Moon and Sun.	En2/2a-d;5a,e,f,g
Engaging with and Responding to Texts	Read stories about space and time.	En2/4a-i
	Read and evaluate newspaper headlines.	En2/5a-g
Creating and Shaping Texts	Compose poems about rocket take-offs.	En3/1a-e;2a-f
	Copy the style of written myths and legends.	En3/1a-e;2a-f;6a,b
Presentation	Present the discovery of a new planet.	En3/1a-e;2a-f; ICT PoS 1a-c;2a-c; 3a,b;4a-c
Maths (Page 46)		
Using and Applying Mathematics	Understand numerical place value in different bases.	Ma2/2a,b,c;4b
Understanding Shape	Know the properties of spheres and other shapes.	Ma3/1h;2a-c
	Recognize which 2-D shapes are used to make 3-D shapes.	Ma3/2d
Measuring	Suggest ways to measure circumferences and diameters of spheres.	Ma3/1a,g,h;4b
	Know that a complete rotation is 360 degrees.	Ma3/2a
Handling Data	Interpret a line graph.	Ma4/2c,f
	Match data to a line graph.	Ma4/2a,f

Earth, Sun and Moon

Learning Objectives	Curriculum References
Design & Technology (Page 48)	
Design and make moving Moon buggies using electricity or elastic bands.	PoS 1a-d;2a-e;3a-c;4a-d;5a-c QCA DT Unit 5C
Use a cam system to make things move.	PoS 2a-e;3a-c;4c; QCA DT Unit 5C
Art (Page 48)	
Use shapes and colour to represent a new planet.	PoS 1a-c;2a-c;3a,b;4a,b;5a-c; QCA Art Unit 5A
Make a container to take from Earth on a space journey.	PoS 1a-c;2a-c;3a,b;4a,b;5a-c; QCA Art Unit 5B
Make a 3-D model of a new planet.	PoS 1a-c;2a-c;3a,b;4a,b;5a-c
PE (Page 48)	
Find solutions to problems on a strange planet.	PoS 1a,b;11a-c; QCA PE Unit 30
Devise a sequence for moving as if on the Moon.	PoS 1a,b;6b
MFL (Page 48)	
Learn vocabulary for units of time.	PoS 1a-d;3a,b,c,e,g; QCA MFL Unit 5
Ask questions about time.	PoS 1a-d; QCA MFL Unit 5
PSHCE (Page 50)	
Select objects/feelings of value to put in a container.	Pos 1a,c; QCA Citizenship Unit 02
Make decisions about what to do when different people live together.	PoS 1a-c;2a,c;3a,4a,c,d,e,f; QCA Citizenship Unit 05
History (Page 50)	
Find out about the first landing on the Moon and events leading to it.	PoS 1a,b;3;4a,b;5a-c
Find out about life in the 1950s–1970s when people travelled into space.	PoS 1a,b;3;4a,b;5a-c; QCA History Unit 20
Debate the beliefs of early sailors about the shape of the Earth.	PoS 2a-c;4a,b
Hold a court inquest into the beliefs of Galileo.	PoS 1a,b;2a-d;4a,b;5a-c
Geography (Page 50)	
Compare sizes of planets and the Sun.	PoS 2c,d,f; QCA Geography Unit 25
Compare distances on Earth.	PoS 2c,d,f; QCA Geography Unit 25
Music (Page 50)	
Listen to space music.	PoS 4a-d; QCA Music Unit 18
Devise music to accompany different planets.	PoS 1b,c;2a,b; 3a-c;5a-d; QCA Music Unit 18

Earth, Sun and Moon

Science

Starting Points

- A familiar type of concept map uses five or six nouns spread over a page. Arrows join pairs of them with words written along the arrows to show the relationship between them. It is useful to teach children how they work by first using a familiar story or rhyme, such as Goldilocks/Red Riding Hood. They can suggest nouns from the story and then join two of them, such as:

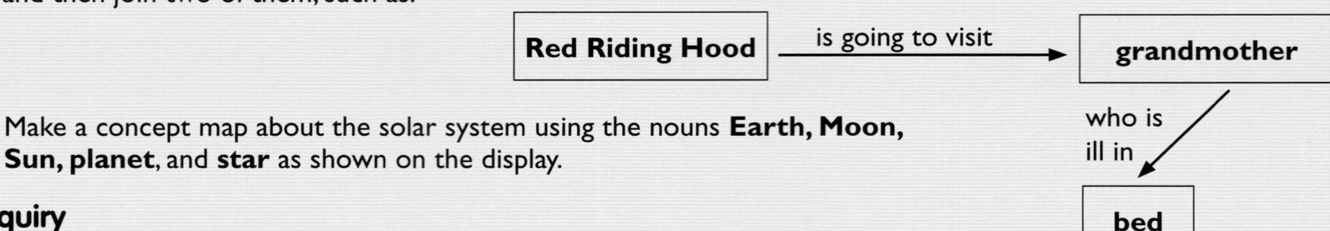

Make a concept map about the solar system using the nouns **Earth, Moon, Sun, planet**, and **star** as shown on the display.

Enquiry

- Before rockets were able to go into space, we had not seen the back of the Moon. Discuss the reasons for this with the children. Select an 'Earthchild' and a 'Moonchild' to demonstrate how this happens.
  - 'Earthchild' rotates slowly on the spot in an anticlockwise direction – one complete rotation represents 24 hours.
  - With 'Earthchild' rotating at the centre, 'Moonchild' revolves slowly in an anticlockwise direction around the Earth, always showing its face to the Earth. One complete revolution represents approximately 28 days, or a lunar month. Discuss the difference between 'rotate' and 'revolve'.
  - Ask the children if the Moon is rotating as it revolves around the Earth. It is. To show this:

    'Moonchild' revolves around the Earth again but stops at each quarter turn. Ask 'Moonchild' to say which wall he is facing at each stop. It is different each time until 'Moonchild' returns to the starting point.

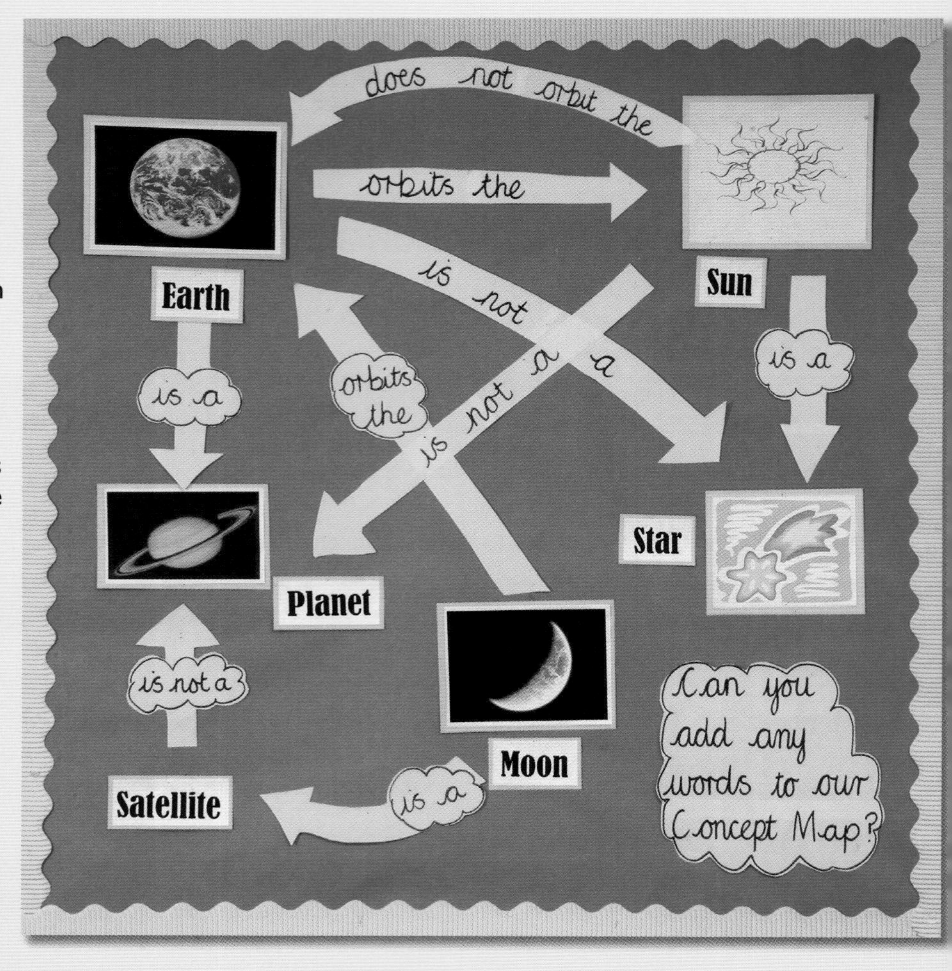

This shows that for each complete revolution round the Earth, the Moon rotates exactly once. That is why we see the same face of the Moon!

Extension Activities

- Investigate how shadows change during the day and at different times of the year. Suggest reasons why.
- Identify times of day by looking at diagrams of Sun. Moon and Earth. See the activity sheet on page 43.

What is the time of day?

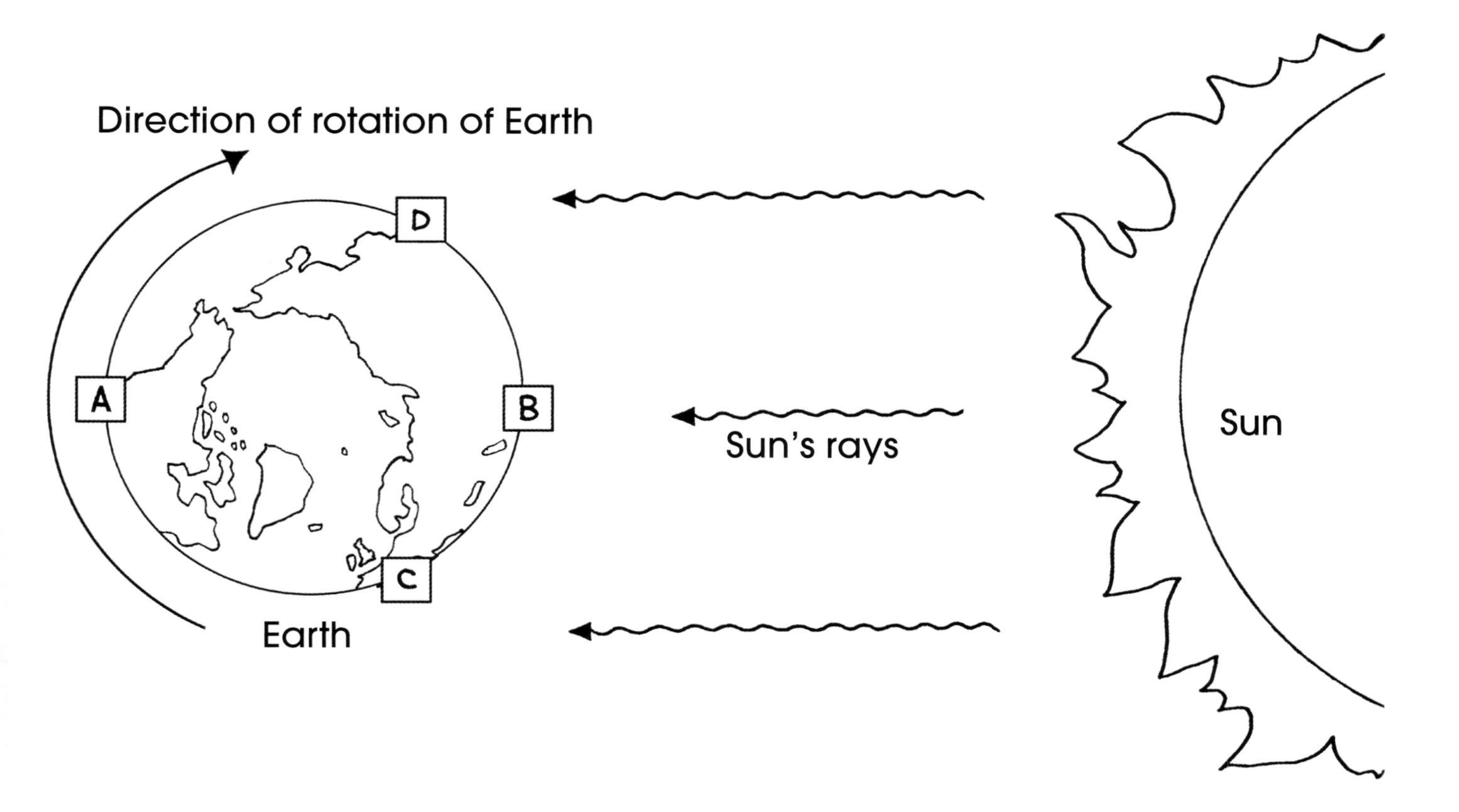

Draw an arrow from each letter to the time of day shown in the diagram.

At A it is	sunset
At B it is:	sunrise
At C it is	midday
At D it is	midnight

NOW!

Choose one of these activities.

1. **Stick a model of yourself on your country on a globe. Move the globe to show how the Earth rotates. Tell someone the approximate time as you rotate the Earth.**
2. **Find out why it gets dark earlier in winter than in summer.**
3. **Keep a record of how the Moon changes shape over two weeks. Does it really change shape? Can you explain what happens?**

Literacy

Speaking and Listening

- Look at headlines of a variety of events in different newspapers. How do they catch people's attention? Read reports/watch videos of an aspect of space exploration. Devise your own report as in the display. Watch the first landing on the Moon by man.
- Ask the children to pretend to interview an astronaut about their journey into space.
- Find out about the daily life of an astronaut in a capsule.
- Ask groups to discuss advantages and disadvantages of space travel. Pros could be that we need to know as much as we can about the Universe to understand more about our Earth, or that the Earth is so overcrowded that we could perhaps live somewhere else. Cons are that it is expensive and may be dangerous – there have already been accidents. Elect a chairman and speakers for a debate. Have a vote, using a ballot box.

Our Class

Lowbrook Advertiser

Read your local newspaper, you know it makes sense.

Lunar Landing

Get your weekly paper now!

Only 50p

Man Meets Moon!

Neil nips to the moon !

Read all about it.

21st July 1969

Yesterday, 20th July, astronaut Neil Armstrong was the first human-being to step foot on the moon. He travelled into space with Buzz Aldrin and Michael Collins along side him. Neil's first words as he made this huge achievement were "This is one small step for man but one giant leap for mankind".

Special offer! $10 off colour TVs A must have item. Amaze your family and friends.

Buy your long -range telescope from Brown's Store. Only $60 . Offer ends this week. Easy payment terms available.

"One small step for man, a giant leap for mankind !"

Their safe arrival was made in 8 Days, 3 hours and 18 minutes. Jennifer Armstrong, Neil's wife, said that she believes in Neil and she is so proud of this great achievement. The three men did this for the president Lyndon Johnston who has always wanted a true American to be the first man or woman to land on the moon. President Lyndon Johnson commented on how proud he was of Neil, Buzz and Michael.

The three astronauts have travelled around in a buggy called Lunar Rover. Mrs Armstrong told us "It had been Neil Armstrong's dream to travel across the moon".

Neil begins his walk on the Moon

Reach for the Stars (and stripes.)

Picture of Neil Armstrong walking on the moon, yesterday.

Neil trained at NASA. Paul Weather, manager of NASA said "I am very happy that one of my astronauts made first step on the moon". An estimated 600 million people were watching him take the first step on the moon. One fifth of the population was the largest for any single event in history to be watched but now it had been beaten by this amazing event.

Reported, as it happens, by our intrepid Sharks class journalists!

Newspaper

Reading and Writing

- Make a glossary of space terms.
- Make up fact files about either the Sun or the Moon.
- Research the beliefs about the Sun or Moon from an ancient civilization such as the Egyptians, Australian Aboriginals, Incas or Greeks.
- Ask the children to imagine a new planet has been discovered. Describe the following aspects, as well as anything else you can think of:
  - the landscape – surface features, the sky
  - weather – variations, temperature
  - plants – structure, variations, life processes
  - animals – variations, life processes, movement, language

  Make up instructions for the crew when they land there.
- Imagine being an astronaut landing on a new planet. Write notes for a diary as on the activity sheet on page 45. The children should create aname for the planet. Notes should not be written in sentences. They can be used to write in another genre later.
- Read *Lost in the solar system* by Joanna Cole (Scholastic), one of the Magic Bus series. Ask the children to pretend to be one of the class on the journey and describe one part of it to someone. Listen to them talking about their part of the journey.

Planet ___________

Fred is one of a team of astronauts to explore planet ________________.

They set off on 24th March and landed on 18th December.

There is official information of the expedition but Fred keeps his own logbook of events on the planet. He writes in note form. Imagine you are Fred and complete the logbook.

date	notes
Saturday **18th December**	Landed safely 08.36. All excited; dust storm outside; no-one outside ship until safe. Cannot see much – dust on windows. John and Jen first out at 11.48; surface spongy; difficult to move. Put flag up. Rest of us out tomorrow with instruments.
Sunday **19th December**	Felt surface; dusty and dry; great jagged stones;
Monday **20th December**	
Tuesday **21st December**	
Wednesday **22nd December**	
Thursday **23rd December**	
Friday **24th December**	

Maths

Using and Applying

- Revise headings for columns when counting in tens. What is the largest digit we use? (9 – then it becomes 10.) Imagine we have only one hand and count in fives. Put column headings – units, 5, 5×5 (25), 5×5×5 (125). Practice writing some numbers in base five. Six is written as '11' – one five and one unit. When children get this idea, practice other bases.
- Computers work on a base two system in which only the digits '0' and '1' are used. Practise counting in base two. Six children stand in a line to represent the heading of columns – units, 2, 4, 8, 16 and 32. Teacher begins to count slowly and when a child has a '1' in his or her column she raises her arm so all can see. For example, if the teacher calls out the number '25', only the children in the units, 8 and 16 columns should have their arms raised, as 16 + 8 + 1 equals 25. Children get quick at this with practice. Ask each child who heads a column what the pattern is for them to raise and lower their arm. Ask the audience what they notice. Change children, change the base to base three and try again.
- Make up space monsters who count in different bases because they have two antennae or three fingers or some other variation. Write the first ten numbers of each of their counting systems as on the display above.
- Look at a range of different sized spheres. Challenge children to measure the circumference and diameter of each as on the activity sheet on page 47. Try to find different ways to do this.

Understanding Shape

- Collect and list as many different spheres around us. Make up a display of them, including photographs of those too big to display.
- Ask groups write as many properties of a sphere as they can. Do they tessellate? Why not? Do the same for other 3-D mathematical shapes.
- Make a collection of other 3-D shapes. In pairs, one child uses mathematical language to describe a 3-D shape to his partner, who tries to guess which it is. Children test themselves with 5 different shapes and try to improve the times they take to guess correctly.
- Show children some 2-D shapes. Ask them to list which of the 3-D shapes could be made of each of the 2-D shapes. For example, a sphere only contains a circle, a cylinder consists of a rectangle and a circle, and a tetrahedron consists of only equilateral triangles. Ensure that when children explain their choices they use correct mathematical language.

How big? How far?

Find these balls and make some measurements of them.

Fill in the measurements on this table.

Type of ball	Circumference		Diameter		Radius	
	in cm	in m	in cm	in m	in cm	in m
Beach ball						
Football						
Orange						
Table tennis ball						

You could use any of these for measuring:

Metre ruler

30 cm ruler

Tape measure

Piece of string

The planets are almost spherical. These are measurements of the diameters of the nine planets to scale.

Mercury	4.9 mm	Saturn	121 mm	Mars	6.7 mm
Venus	12 mm	Uranus	51 mm	Pluto	2 mm
Earth	13 mm	Neptune	49 mm	Jupiter	143 mm

Put them in order of size from largest to smallest.

Find some spherical shapes around you that are about the same sizes as these plantets to scale. For example, a cherry for the Earth. You could make some up using Plasticine.

Put your planets in order going away from the Sun.

Design & Technology

- Make a Moon buggy that will move either by electricity or by elastic bands. Children may either use construction kits or make their own frameworks. To drive the buggy, attach an electric circuit with a motor and elastic band around an axle, or use a stretched elastic band to wind round the rear axle. See the activity sheet on page 49 for instructions for an elastic band version.
- Test the buggy. How far will it go? How can the speed be altered? Can it go uphill? What if the surface is changed?
- Make a space monster that can move a part of its body using a cam system.

Art

- Use colouring materials such as paint, chalk and charcoal to represent the landscape of a mysterious new planet. Use a variety of techniques to add texture and atmosphere.
- Represent the landscape of a mysterious new planet in a box, using 3-D objects and materials. Decorate the outside of the box with the name of the planet, the sky and the surroundings. Supply a net, or get the children to draw a net for the box.

PE

- Move as if on the Moon, varying speed and direction. Link to science.
- Show children a hammer and a feather. Predict what will happen to them when you drop them. Ask what would happen to them if you let them go on the Moon. Ideas may include 'stay where they are', 'go into space' or 'fall in the same way as on Earth'. Watch a clip of Neil Armstrong doing this activity on the Moon (available at www.youtube.com/watch?v=dHzVsLAhUCA). They fall at the same rate. Discuss why this happens. Further information is available at www.videos.howstuffworks.com/nasa.

MFL

- Learn vocabulary for different units of time. Groups should make a display for each of the seasons with the names of the seasons and months in response to *Quelle est la saison?*, *Quel est le mois?* and *Quelle est la date?* or equivalent in other languages. See the display in which a special date is given for each season. Children should find out what happened on that date and learn vocabulary related to it. They should link this to work about why we have changing seasons and the position of the earth.

Make a moving Moon buggy

You will need:

- Thick corrugated cardboard, like a supermarket box.
- Old CDs for wheels
- Cut up outside of used pens to stabilize the wheels on the axle
- Thin dowel or garden sticks for axles
- Pegs to hold the axles so they can spin freely
- A paperclip
- Elastic bands
- Some strong quick drying glue.

It will look like this.

1. To make the chassis (base), cut out a long strip of corrugated card and strengthen it with another piece along the centre with the corrugation in a different direction. This makes it even stronger.

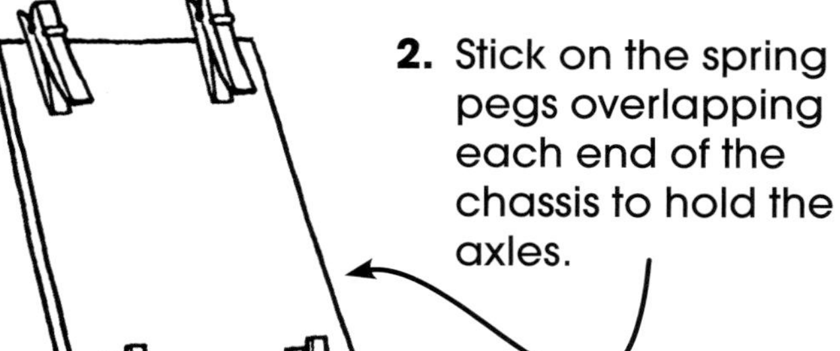

2. Stick on the spring pegs overlapping each end of the chassis to hold the axles.

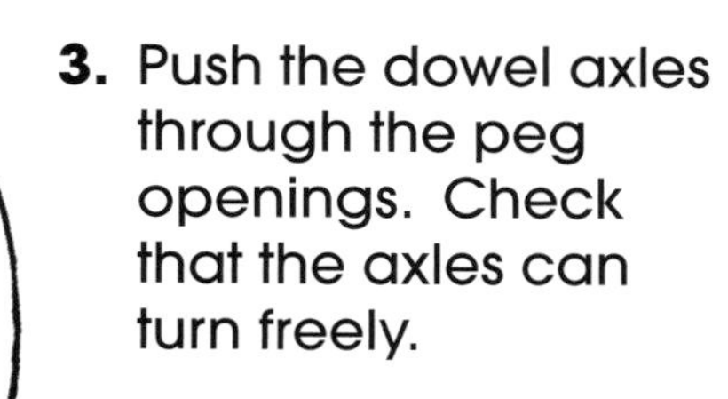

3. Push the dowel axles through the peg openings. Check that the axles can turn freely.

4. To make the wheels – stick a piece of card over the centre of the CD and make a hole in it just wide enough for the axle. Cut out short pieces of the outside of the pen and stick either side of the centre of the card on the CD. Attach wheels to the axles. The pen pieces hold the wheels firm. Ensure the wheels turn with the axle and do not move freely on it.

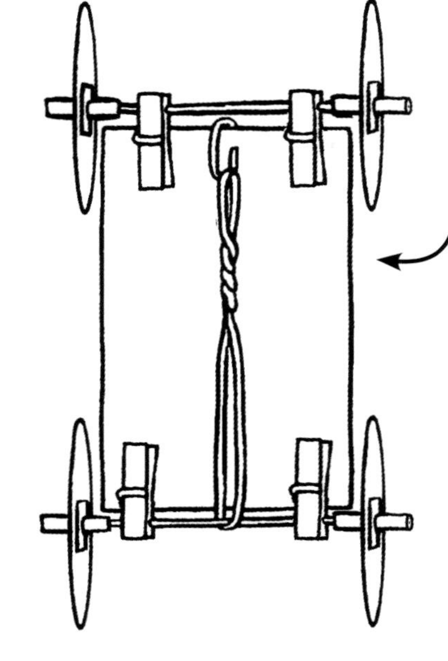

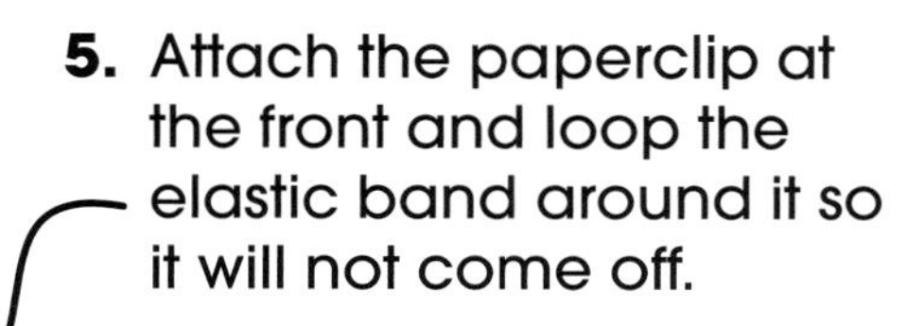

5. Attach the paperclip at the front and loop the elastic band around it so it will not come off.

6. Stretch the band around the back axle and let go on a rough surface.As the back axle turns, so do the wheels and the Moon buggy will go.

How far does it go? How could you make it go further or faster?

PSHCE

- The Sun's rays can be dangerous if we are not protected. Ask the children to find out the different ways we should protect ourselves, as shown on the display. Make up a catchy slogan to make people think about the dangers. Consider other ways of persuading people to stay safe.
- Look at labels on sunscreen to find out what each promises. Which do children think will offer the most protection?
- In pairs: one child plays the role of a sun worshipper; the other should argue the importance of protecting against the Sun's rays.

History

- Many explorers of the past believed that the Earth was flat. Act out a play involving leaving home, sailing into unknown territory, and the fear of falling off the edge of the Earth. The children could write or talk about what they expect to find when they come to the edge of the Earth.
- Make up a time line to show the development of space exploration.
- Find out about the beliefs of Galileo Galilei (1564–1642) and how he was treated. Hold a 'trial' with people questioning him about his beliefs.

Geography

- Look at photographs that show the Earth, the Sun and Moon. Estimate then find out the distances between each of them. Do the same with the diameters and circumferences of each.
- Look at maps of places on Earth at different scales. The children should use the scales and measurement to calculate distances between countries, around the equator, from one town to another in their own country, or from home to school. Include many different distances. Children can decide on their own distances to measure.

Music

- Listen to famous pieces of music about space such as *The planets* by Gustav Holst (1874–1934), *Space oddity* by David Bowie (b. 1947) or *War of the worlds* by Jeff Wayne (b. 1943). Find others and select two contrasting pieces. How does each make the children feel? Why?
- We cannot hear sounds in space as there is no atmosphere to carry the vibrations. It is silent. However, where there is an atmosphere, sounds can be heard. Ask the children to imagine a newly discovered planet with an atmosphere that could be any mixture of gases. Decide on what sort of planet it could be – funny, frightening or mysterious – and the types of sound that would describe it best. Make up three contrasting sounds – long/short; high/low; loud/quiet. The children could devise their own symbols for music. Make up a short piece of space music, using the activity sheet on page 51. Combine the music in parts to describe different planets.

My musical planet

This is the planet discovered on 4th July 2056. The astronauts have named it Zog. The sky is red, the surface green and there is a slimy sort of purple liquid about. The astronauts think there are living things here as there is an atmosphere of gases and possibly water.

The astronauts hear sounds there. They are quite mysterious.

This is how one of the astronauts drew the sounds:

Play this music, choosing suitable instruments, your voice and other sounds with your body.

Draw your own planet and make up music for it. Play it for others to listen to.

Changing Sounds

These grids demonstrate the learning objectives covered in the activities within the theme. The curriculum references indicate the relevant programme of study (PoS) for a subject area unless otherwise stated.

	Learning Objectives	Curriculum References
Science (Page 54)		
Scientific Enquiry	Investigate how and why scientists such as edison and bell worked to make important discoveries.	Sc1/1a
	Predict and hypothesise using experience and knowledge.	Sc1/2c
	Carry out fair tests on hearing.	Sc1/2a-m
	Investigate home-made telephones.	Sc1/2a-m
Physical Processes (QCA Science Unit 5F)	Find out how sound travels through different media from one place to another.	Sc4/3e
	Learn that sound is made by vibrating materials.	Sc4/3e,g
	Discover how sound travels through solids, liquids and gases.	Sc4/3e,g
	Identify ways in which volume and pitch can be changed.	Sc4/3f
Breadth of Study	Find out how loud sounds affect hearing.	Sc2b
Life Processes	Compare ears of different animals and relate to lifestyle.	Sc2/5c
Materials and their Properties	Understand which materials are good at insulating sound.	Sc3/1a
Literacy (Page 56)		
Speaking	Use voice to make a variety of noises to express feelings.	En1/1a,b
Listening and Responding	Evaluate writing or speaking of others in class.	En1/2a-e;3a,b;6c;9a
Drama	Devise and act out a play about sound.	En1/1f;4a-d;8a-c;9a-c
Word Structure and Spelling	Recognize and use homophones.	En3/4a,c,d,j
Creating and Shaping Texts	Compose poems about a particular sound or a mixture of sounds, using a variety of stimuli and silence.	En3/1a-e;2a-f;5a,b;9a;12
	Write instructions for making a musical instrument. .	En3/1a,c,d,e; 6a;9b
Understanding and Interpreting Texts	Read a variety of poetry forms to inform writing.	En2/4a
Mathematics (Page 58)		
Measuring	Measure the level of sounds in various places and at different times.	Ma3/1a;4a,b; ICT PoS 1a;4a-c; QCA ICT Unit 5F
	Select appropriate measuring instruments.	Ma3/4b
	Measure distances and convert metres and centimetres to decimals and fractions.	Ma3/4a,b; Ma2/2d,f
	Use measurement in comparing distances and sound volume.	Ma3/4a,b
Handling Data	Construct and interpret graphs and measurements when carrying out investigations.	Ma4/1a-h;2a,b,c,e,f
	Select appropriate graphs for collected data.	Ma4/2c,e
	Convert data to graphs on a computer.	ICT PoS 1b,c

Learning Objectives	Curriculum References
Design & Technology (page 60)	
Construct musical instruments to blow, shake, strike and pluck.	PoS 1a-d; 2a-e; 3a-c; 4a; QCA DT Unit 5A
Make and investigate telephones.	PoS 2a-d; 3a,b;
Make bangers.	PoS 3a,b
Art (page 62)	
Select designs and colours for musical instruments.	PoS 1a,b; QCA Art unit 5A
PSHCE (page 62)	
Consider effects of noise in the environment.	PoS 1c; 2a; 5a
List people who should protect their hearing and how they do it.	PoS 2a,f; 3a
Find ways to send secret sound messages from one place to another.	PoS1a-d;2a-e;3b
Learn about being deaf and how to communicate with deaf people.	PoS 1a;5e,f
Geography (page 62)	
Explore musical instruments played in Britain by people from different nationalities.	PoS 3a-c; 2c; QCA Ge Unit 24
Find different ways in which messages are sent across the world.	PoS 1b,c; QCA Ge Unit 18
History (page 62)	
Study musical instruments from different times.	PoS 4a; 5a
Find out about the invention of the telephone.	PoS 4a,b; 5a-c; 8a,b; 11a
Compare the ways messages are sent now and in past times.	PoS 1a,b; 11b
PE (page 62)	
Design movement to accompany voice sounds.	PoS 6a,b; QCA PE Unit 21
Music (page 62)	
Devise sounds and/or lyrics.	PoS 1b,c; 2a,b; QCA Music Unit 19
Make up own annotation for music.	PoS 2a,b; QCA Music Unit 19
Explore how music is made in different instruments.	PoS 1b; 4b,c
Explore the difference between noise and music.	PoS 3a,b

Changing Sounds

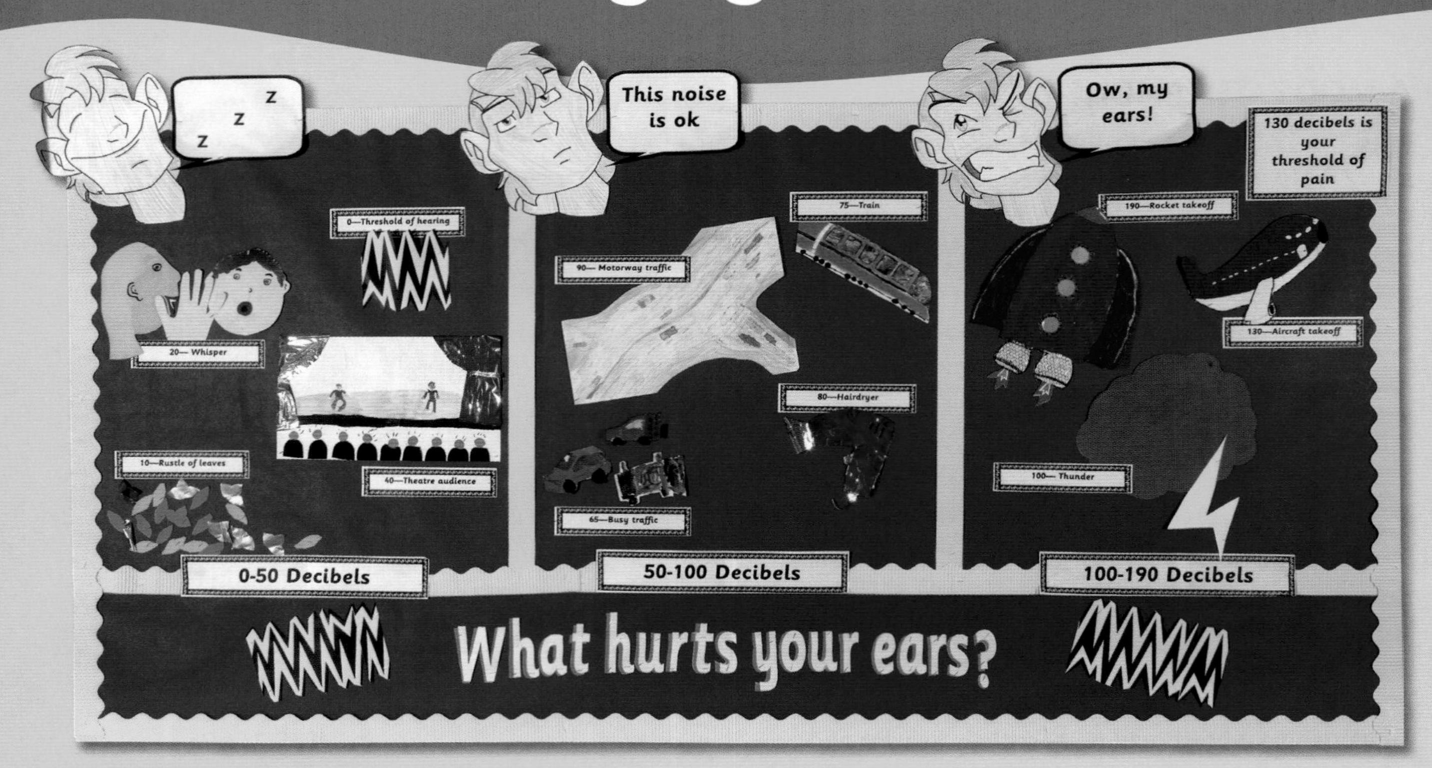

Science

Starting Points

- Talk about hearing and its importance to us and how loud sounds can affect it. Find out how we measure the level of sound. Make a display like the one on this page to show how loud different sounds are. Discuss what happens when we are subjected to loud sounds over a period of time.

Enquiry

- Make music! Choose a range of musical instruments – blown, shaken, plucked and struck – and make up a short sequence of sounds.
- Challenge the children to find ways of changing the loudness of one of them. Come to a generalization, such as 'the harder I hit/blow/pluck/shake, the louder the sound.' Is this true for all instruments, or for sounds made on other things? Relate the size of the vibrations to loudness.
- Investigate ways to change the pitch of a string. String may be on a real instrument (CARE NEEDED!) or an elastic band, string or wire wrapped around a box. Hypothesise and test. Factors to try: length (changed by putting a pencil under the band to change the length that vibrates); tightness (different lengths of elastic band); material (string, wool, bands, wires); thickness of string. Observe how vibrations change and make a generalization such as 'the tighter the string, the higher the note. The faster it vibrates the higher the note.'

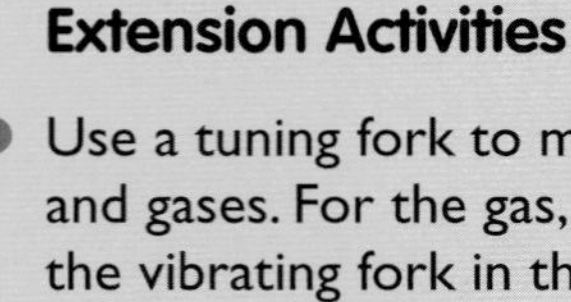

Extension Activities

- Use a tuning fork to make a sound. Compare how well its sound travels through solids and gases. For the gas, use air. For a liquid, place one ear in a bowl of water and place the vibrating fork in the water. Can be repeated at home with other sounds in the bath. Sounds travel much better through liquids and solids than through gases.
- Play Chinese whispers and compare the final message with the original. Does the size of the group affect the outcome?
- Make cones to represent large ears, and compare how well we hear with and without them. Where have children seen cones like this used? See the activity sheet on page 55.

Telephones

A MODEL TELEPHONE

Your task: To send a 'sound message' to a friend using a home made telephone

Make up your model telephone so it looks like the one that Susan and Rachid are using.

They used paper cups with string between them.

They attached the string like this:

Send a message to a friend and listen to the reply.

How well does your telephone work?

Make the best possible telephone that works when you are 5 metres apart.

Try changing each of these in turn to find out what makes a difference:

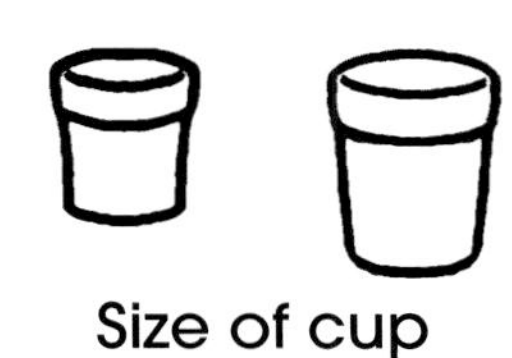

Size of cup

How tight the thread is

Material of cup

Material of the thread between the cups

Can you think of anything else?

Now test some telephones!

Write instructions for making the best telephone from the materials you have used.

Compare your results with others. Do you all agree?

1 Make a four way telephone.

2 Make a telephone that works around corners.

3 How far can you send a message with your telephone?

Literacy

Reading and Writing

- List a variety of sounds that could be heard in the playground. Ask each child to write a line about one of the sounds. Put together as a group or class to make up a poem as on the display. Think about the best words to use, rather than worrying about rhyming.
- Describe sounds around us. Words could be made up – jaggedy, muffaluff – or real words. Use the words to make up a sound poem using only the sounds on the list. Recite the poems, using intonation and expression to add interest.
- Select a familiar sound and make up a poem about it that repeats the sound; for example, drip-drop for rain; fizz, fizz for a fizzy drink or a firework; tick-tock for a clock.

- Write instructions, using the imperative mood, for making a sound model, such as a paper banger, a bull roarer or a musical instrument (link with Design & Technology – see page 60).
- Use interesting typescripts to make up advertising posters for plays. The stars should have 'sound' names, for example *The silent scream* starring Rob Roarer, Beryl Bellow and Mike Mutter.

Speaking and Listening

- Make up an interview to carry out with a person of choice. The interview could be with an actual person, or could be an imaginary one with a person from the past. The interview could be about a noise issue in the community, or talking to Alexander Graham Bell (1847–1922) about his work, a doctor who examines hearing problems or a person who works with deaf people.
- Hold a debate about the proposed building of a factory, new road or airport runway in the local area. Put forward the advantages and disadvantages.

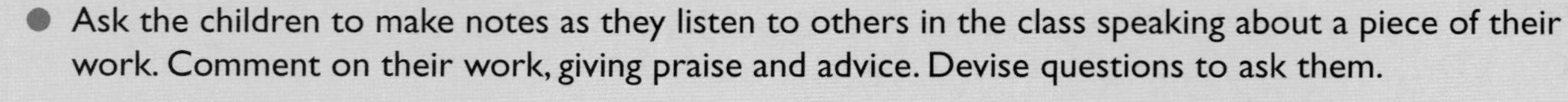

- Ask the children to make notes as they listen to others in the class speaking about a piece of their work. Comment on their work, giving praise and advice. Devise questions to ask them.

- Prepare a class assembly about sound which includes different subjects. Remember that sounds can be quiet as well as loud!
- Find out about homophones (words that have different meanings but sound the same) and use them in sentences as shown on the activity sheet on page 57. The answers to the riddles on the activity sheet are as follows:

1. Blew and blue
2. Horse and hoarse
3. Leek and leak.

Homophones Sound the Same!

'Aloud' and **'allowed'** are homophones. They sound the same, but are spelt differently and have different meanings.

The robot was **allowed** to speak **aloud** after Josh mended his voice box.

Look at these words. They all have at least one homophone. Write their homophones next to them. Try to find more than one other homophone if you can. The first one is done for you.

seem (seam)	feet ______________	their ______________
scent ______________	groan ______________	past ______________
knows ______________	who's ______________	principal ______________

Choose three of the words above and their homophones. Make an interesting sentence using each pair of homophones like this: 'The **seam** on her dress came undone but it did not **seem** to bother her.'

You could decorate your homophones too.

Homophone Riddles!

Here are some riddles. The solutions to each riddle are two homophones. Can you work out what they are?

1. If the wind did this, it would make a water colour.
2. This animal has a problem with its voice.
3. The emblem of Wales drips water.

Find other homophones and make up some riddles of your own about them. Use them in sentences.

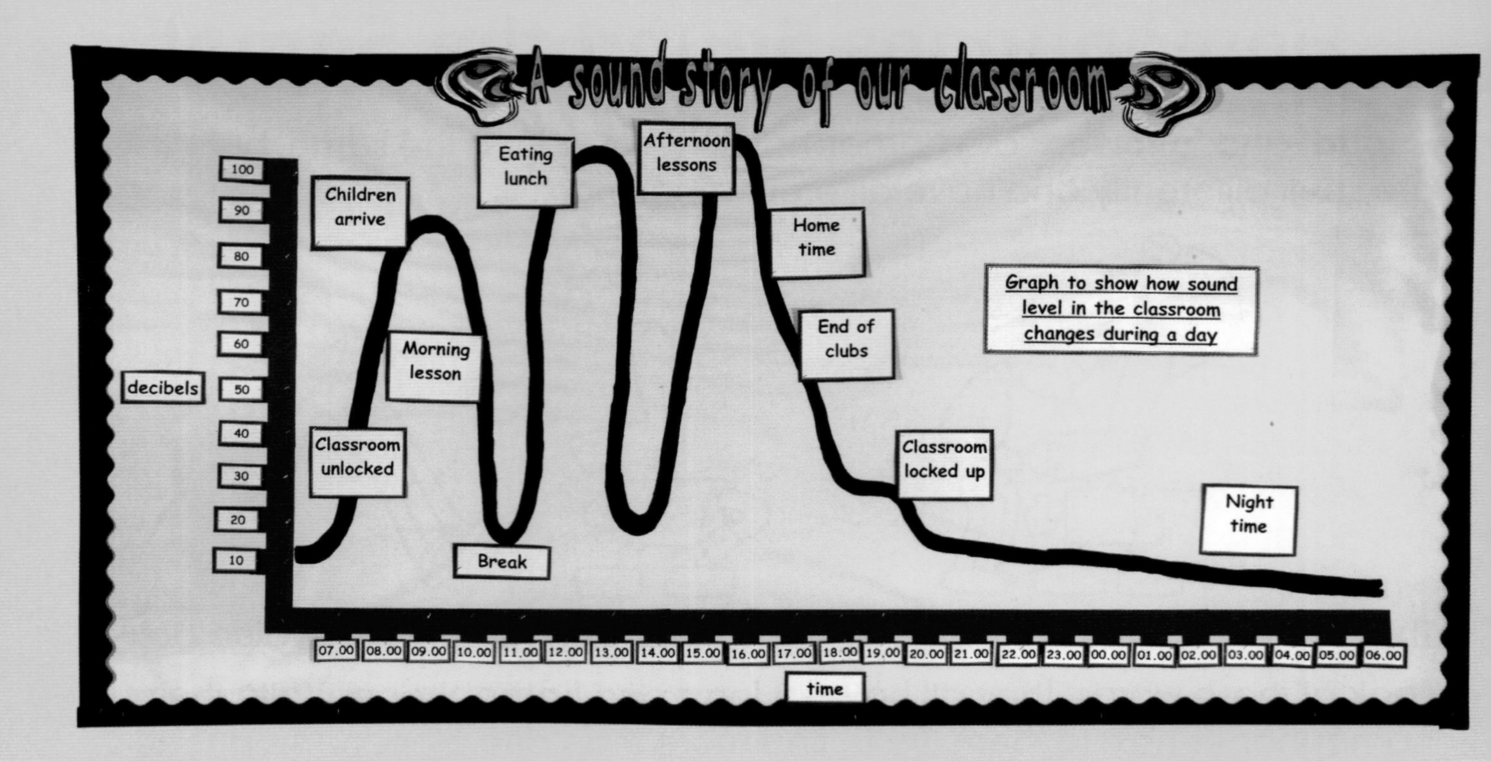

Maths

Measuring

- Record and compare the volume of traffic noise in a particular place throughout the day.
- Compare how well we hear using one ear and two ears. A child sits and a quiet sound (a pin dropped onto a tin) is made behind them. The child should listen, first with one ear, then the other, and finally with both. Measure in centimetres how far away and in which direction the child can hear the sound using each ear and both ears. Convert centimetres to metres as a decimal and a vulgar fraction. Record results on a bar graph for all children in the group. Interpret the graph and suggest reasons for differences. Why is a bar graph better than a line graph for this investigation?
- Investigate how the pitch of an instrument changes with the length of a string. Complete a table. Discuss why results cannot be recorded as a graph. (There is no measurement of the outcome as a number – simply a judgement of pitch).

Handling Data

- Compare sound levels in different places around the school at different times of day. If sensors are not available, children could make a judgement and mark it on a graph to show whether the level is greater or less than the previous time they listened. Children should construct their own line graphs from their data, like the one above. Sequence places from quietest to noisiest at a particular time of day. For the noisiest places, does it help to place a 'Quiet Please' poster there?
- Collect data about sound around us. Discuss why the first is a bar graph and the second a line graph.
  1. How many times we hear a particular sound in a minute. In the classroom try sounds such as a chair scraping, noise from the class next door, someone coughing or sneezing or talking. Transfer information into a bar graph. Children should then devise questions about it.
  2. Monitor the change in sound volume in a place in the school at different times of day. This could be an arbitrary measurement. If possible, use a sound sensor to produce a line graph. Interpret the graph and suggest reasons why variations occur.

Sound information

Here are examples of a line graph and a bar graph. Both display data relating to sound.

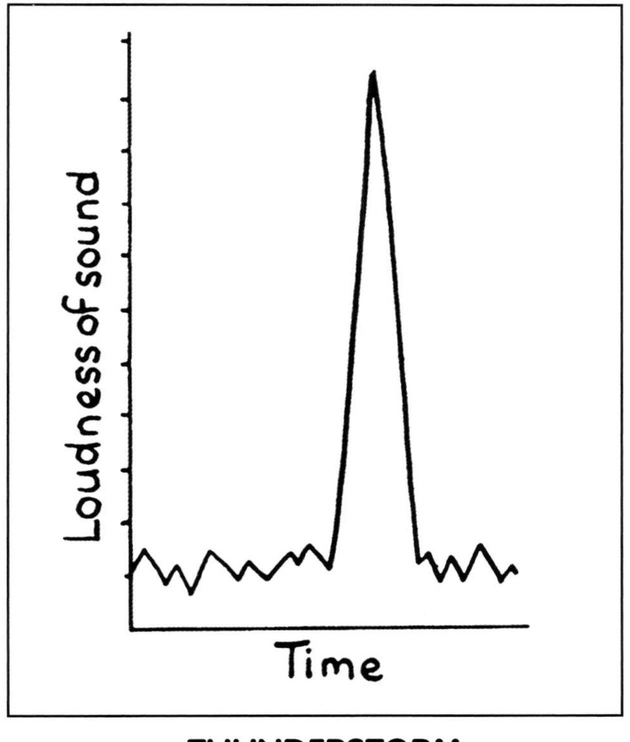

THUNDERSTORM

Why does the line go up in the middle?

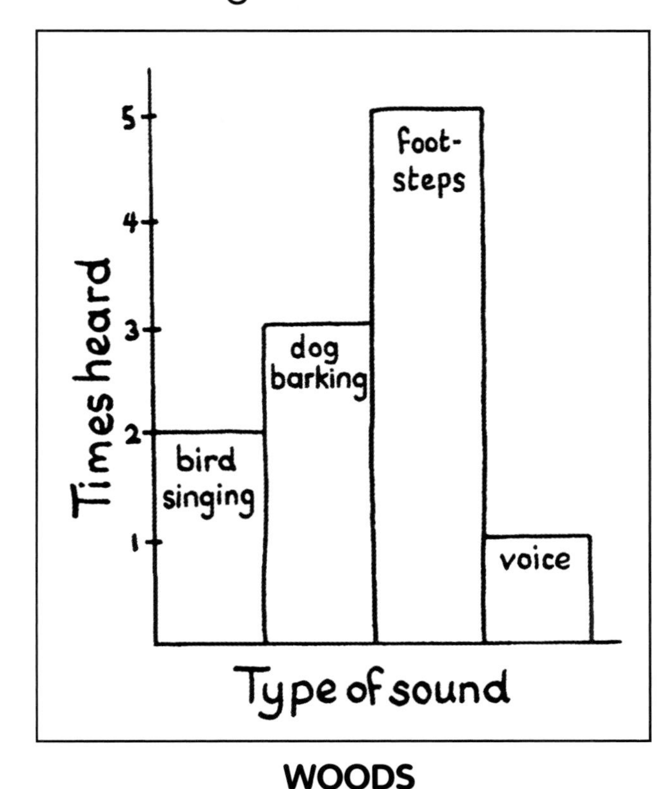

WOODS

How many sounds does he hear in total?

Here are some questions children asked about sound.

- What sounds do we hear in the hall during the day?
- What happens to the sound level when someone sneezes?
- How does the noise of traffic change during the day?
- How many instruments are played by tapping, blowing, striking, plucking?
- How does the length of the string make a difference to the pitch of a note on a guitar?

They tried to make up graphs from their results.

Think of the data they would collect.

Which questions gave data that could be represented as:

A line graph **A bar graph** **No graph at all**

Investigate one of the questions to make sure you have chosen the right sort of graph.

Make up some questions to investigate on your own.

Decide if you can make a graph of your results. If so, what type is best?

Design & Technology

Art

- Use found materials to construct different musical instruments:
  - To blow: glass bottles or jars with varying amounts of water in them. Compare the pitch of the sound when blowing across the top and tapping.

    Make a paper straw recorder.

    Cut the end of the straw into a blunt V-shape Squeeze the ends together to leave only a small gap. Put quite a length into the mouth and blow gently to make a sound. The shorter and wider the straw, the easier it is to make the sound. Cut holes in the straw to make three different notes. It takes practice to blow these paper straws.
  - To shake: various containers with different fillings of varying hardness to create different sounds. Copy tambourines and bells.
  - To pluck: stretch an elastic band around a box. Pluck it. Compare sounds made by bands of varying lengths and thicknesses. Alter how tight each band is and compare the sounds made.
  - To strike: make drums of different sizes from various containers, using paper or balloons for surfaces. Hypothesise what will happen if the tightness of the surface is changed.
  - For all of the above, observe and relate to real instruments.

- Make bangers: see the worksheet on page 61.
- Find ways to send secret sound messages from one place to another.

PSHCE

- Discuss senses and the importance of hearing in our lives. Find out about deafness and what can cause it. List people who should protect their hearing with ear defenders. Examine various types of ear defenders, and try to make some using available materials. Test their effectiveness.
- Mike and Joss go to a disco each week. The music is very loud. Discuss how this might affect their hearing as they get older. What should they do to protect their hearing while still enjoying themselves? Hold a class debate.

Make A Banger!

Wake everyone up with a paper banger!

You will need:

A double sheet from a newspaper – that's all!

Fold the paper as shown.

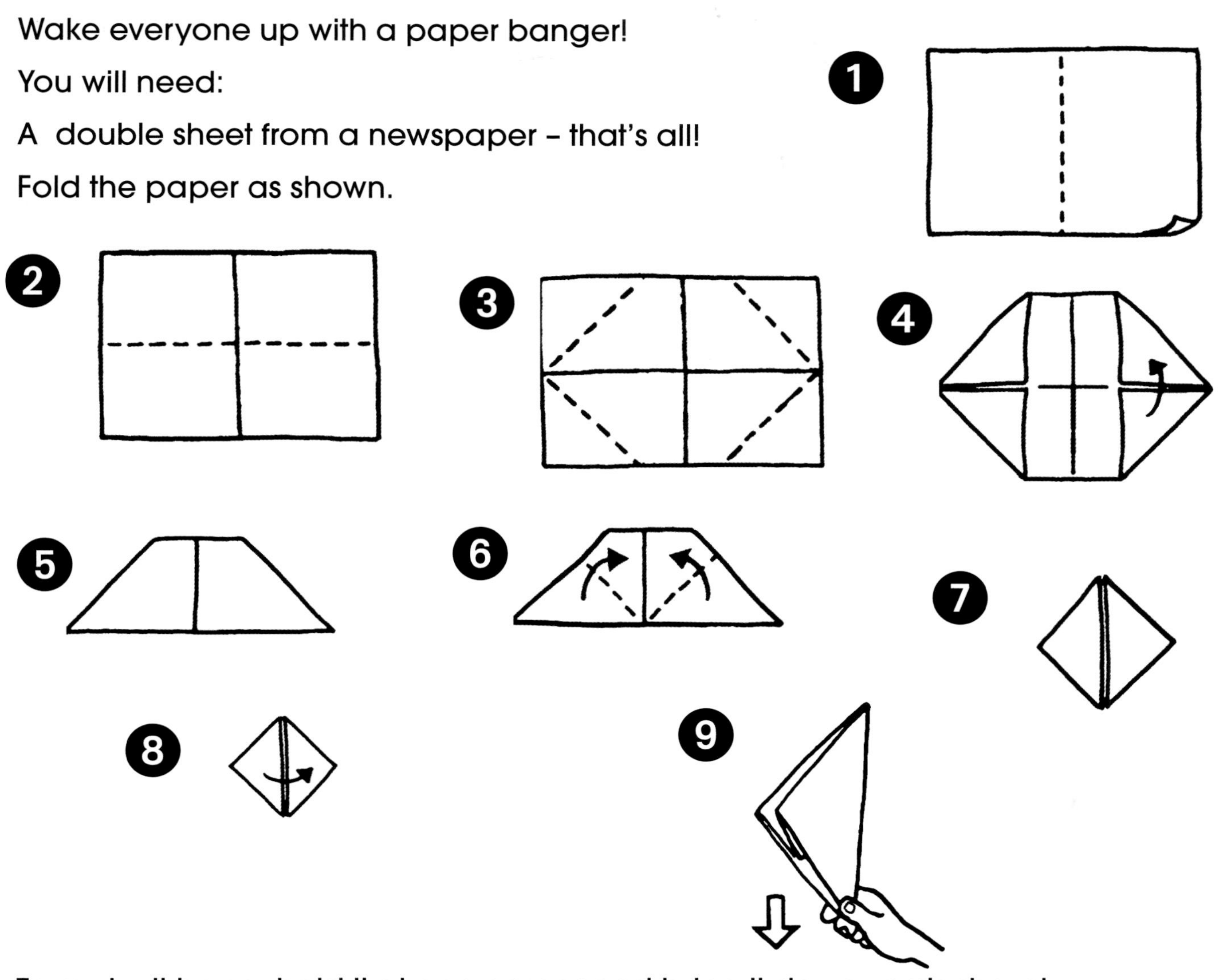

To make it bang: hold it at one corner and bring it downwards sharply.

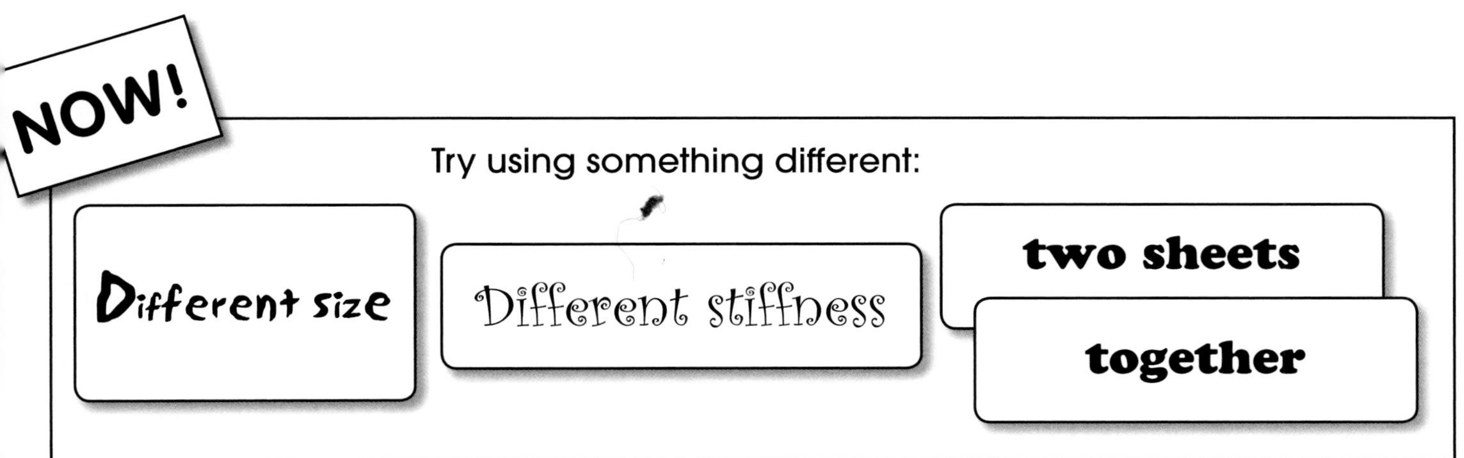

Can you think of anything else to try?

Who can make the loudest bang? Explain to a friend how the bang is made and how you hear it. Remember to use the word 'vibrate'.

Geography

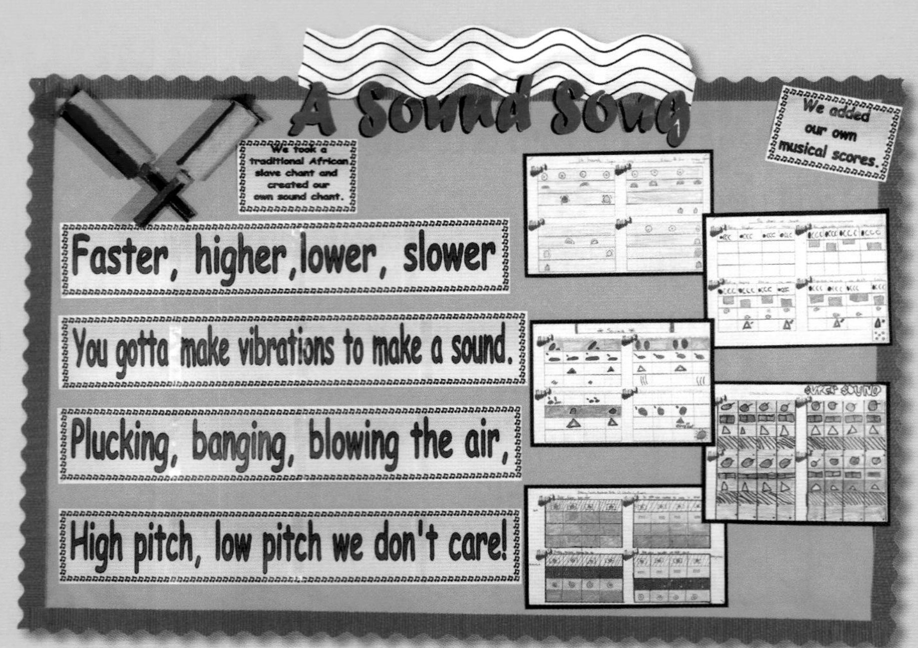

- Explore musical instruments from different cultures. Find the countries they come from on the map. Invite musicians to school to introduce their music. Link with music.
- Study different ways in which sound messages are sent throughout the world. Communicate in different ways with a school in another part of the country or the world – by e-mail, telephone, webcam, letters and so on. Which methods use sound? Is there an advantage in using sound rather than the written word? Share experiences and ways of life.

History

- Find out the importance of music to past civilizations. Find out the names of musical instruments that were used and how they were played. Which current instruments are they like?
- Compare methods of communication used today and in the past – telephones, faxes, computers, letters, talking, semaphore, Morse code, newspapers, magazines and so on. Set up a time line to show when each was introduced.
- Find out about the life of a pioneer of sound, such as Alexander Graham Bell (1847–1922). Thomas Edison (1847–1931) or Gugliemo Marconi (1874–1937).

PE

- Make up a sound poem using voices and/or instruments. It should have no words, only sounds. Move arms, bodies and legs to the changing sounds. Encourage the use of different tempos, pitches and volumes and appropriate body movements. Encourage the free expression of how the music makes each child feel.
- Move to music from different cultures or historical periods. Include contrasting musical pieces for different feelings.

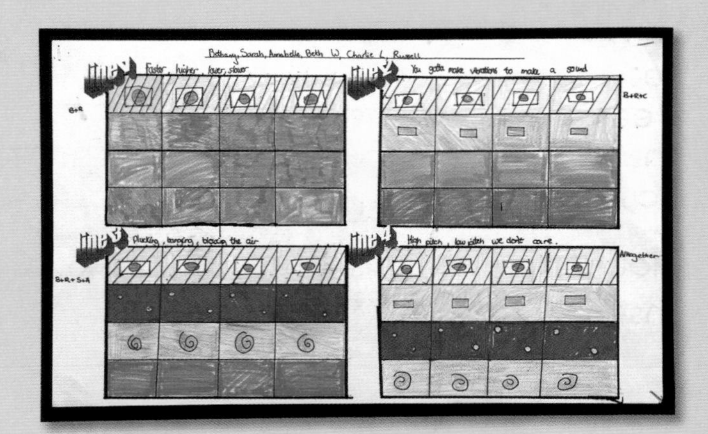

Music

- Compose a sound song – either words to a song composed by children, or symbols to show a sequence of sounds and patterns to be followed along with the music. Show high/low, loud/quiet, short/long, smooth/staccato sounds. See the display on this page and the activity sheet on page 63.
- Group work – children should make a mixture of noises using a variety of objects, instruments and their own bodies. Make up a short piece of music. Elect a child in the group as conductor to conduct each section, while others identify what they think is the difference between noise and music. Children should comment on each other's efforts.

How does it make you feel?

Here is a poem.

The words in brackets show how some children accompanied it.

Who is whispering?

The small breeze
rustling the leaves
on the tree, the sea
calmly welcoming
children in to play
and my baby brother
mumbling to his toes.

(quiet sounds using whispers of voices and brush on drum etc)

Who is talking?

The wind blowing
leaves off the trees
into a whirling
colourful mass, the sea
as it rolls grumbling into
shore and my baby brother in
the morning asking for his breakfast.

(quiet talking, odd notes and chimes)

Who is shouting?

The wind on a stormy
night whistling and
tearing branches off the
trees, the sea monster
thundering ferociously as it tosses the lifeboat into the air, and my baby brother
screaming when he can't get his own way.

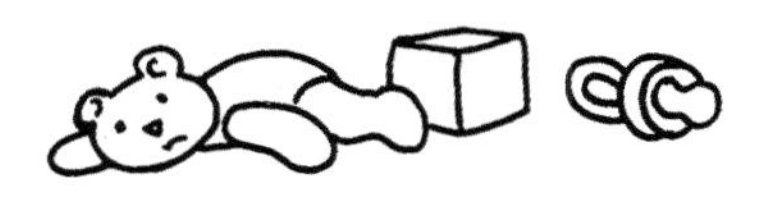

(louder noises – still need to hear the words; end with a combination of all
instruments, building up the sound with no words)

NOW!

Start with the same questions and make up your own answers and accompaniments.

Gases Around Us

These grids demonstrate the learning objectives covered in the activities within the theme. The curriculum references indicate the relevant programme of study (PoS) for a subject area unless otherwise stated.

	Learning Objectives	Curriculum References
Science (Page 66)		
Scientific Enquiry	Enquiry into amount of air in different soils.	Sc1/2a-m
	Gather information about the purity of local air.	Sc1/2a-m
Materials and their Properties (QCA Science Unit 5C)	Find differences and similarities between solids, liquids and gases.	Sc3/1e
	Know properties of some gases, including air.	Sc3/1a
	Identify properties of soils.	Sc3/1d
	Know the part played by air in burning.	Sc3/2b,g
Literacy (Page 68)		
Speaking/Group Discussion and Interaction	Hold a debate about windfarms.	En1/3a-f
Drama	Make up a drama about gases in acid rain and their effect.	En1/4a-d
Understanding and Interpreting Texts	Find incidents of accidents that have polluted the air.	En2/3a-d
	Find out about problems with burning bonfires.	En2/3a,b,d
	Find information on the Internet to support an argument.	ICD PoS 1a-c
Creating and Shaping Texts	Explore and create different poem structures about air, wind, bubbles and burning.	En3/1a-e;2a-f;12
	Present an argument in letters and leaflets.	En3/1a-e;2a-f;6a,b;9b
Presentation	Present information in a variety of ways	En3/1a-e;6a;9b
Mathematics (Page 70)		
Using and Applying Mathematics	Solve everyday problems of volume and other measurements.	Ma3/1a-h
Understanding shape	Recognize properties of 2-D and 3-D shapes.	Ma3/2a-c
	Draw nets of 3-D shapes.	Ma1/2b-d
	Draw mathematical shapes on the computer.	ICT PoS 2b
Measuring	Measure volume in imperial and metric measures.	Ma3/1a; 4a,b
	Convert measures.	Ma3/4a

Gases Around Us

Learning Objectives	Curriculum References
Design & Technology (Page 72)	
Make artificial soil.	PoS 2c,f
Make bubble blowers of different shapes.	PoS 1a-d;2a-f;3a-c;4a-d;5a-c
Make mobiles for a baby's cot.	PoS 1a-d;2a-f;3a-c;4a-d;5a-c
Design and make simple kites.	PoS 1a-d;2a-f;3a-c;4a-d;5a-c
Art (Page 72)	
Look at paintings of LS Lowry and others who painted English towns and pollution.	PoS 4c;5a-d
Represent pollution in own ways.	PoS 1a-c;2a-c;3a,b;4a,b;5a-d
Make soil paintings.	PoS 2a-c
PSHCE (Page 72)	
Recognise the effects of pollution on health.	PoS 2a,k
Suggest ways to reduce pollution.	PoS 1a;2a
Find out how the local area deals with pollution.	PoS 1a,e;5a
Know the effects of smoking on health.	PoS 3a;5d
Music (Page 72)	
Show how blown instruments produce and change sound.	PoS 1b;4b,c; QCA Music Unit 15
Compose and learn bubble songs and accompany.	PoS 1a-c;2a,b;3a-c;4a-d;5a-c; QCA Music Unit 19
Write accompaniments to pictures by artists, or own pictures.	PoS 1a-c;2a,b;3a-c;4a-d;5a-c
History (Page 74)	
The history of ballooning – hot air and hydrogen balloons.	PoS 1a,b,5a-c
Geography (Page 74)	
Identify cities on a map or globe.	PoS 2c
Estimate distances.	PoS 3b
Describe landscapes.	PoS 3a-c
Causes and effects of acid rain.	PoS 1a-e;2d,g;3a,b,e
Discuss a topical issue about pollution locally.	PoS 1a-e;2a,c,f,g; QCA Geography Units12 & 20
PE (Page 74)	
Move like particles in a solid, liquid and gas.	PoS 6a
Compare the effect of air resistance on running and throwing.	PoS 10b; QCA PE Unit 18
Describe lifestyles of sportsmen.	PoS 4c

Gases Around Us

Science

Starting points

- Investigate children's understanding of 'gases'. They may only have the idea that gas is a fuel used for cooking. Show them a helium balloon and ask what makes it stay up. What is inside it? What surrounds it? Try to name other gases. Groups should research one gas, note where they could find it and discover three of its properties. Devise characters for each gas and display them. One way is shown on the display above.

Enquiry

- Discuss air as a mixture of gases, and where air occurs. Focus on soils for an enquiry.
- Collect at least 3 different soils with different properties – a sandy soil (large particles), a clay soil (small particles), or soil from a woodland or similar that has a lot of vegetation in it. Children should use their senses to describe each soil. Look at them with magnifiers and sort out different parts of each soil. Some may have living organisms in them. List all the things that could be found in soil and discuss where soil has come from.
- For each soil, predict if there will be air in it. Give each group a cup of any of the soils. Mark the level of the soil on the cup. Children should pack the soil down as much as they can. What is now missing?
- Give each group equal cupfuls of each soil. They should measure water in a measuring cylinder and pour it slowly into each of the cups until no more can be absorbed and a thin layer of water is visible on the top of the soil. Note the bubbles coming up. Record how much water is absorbed by each type of soil – what does this tell us about the amount of air in each one? Which soil has the most air in it? Where does the air go when the water is added?
- Try mixing soils together and comparing the amount of air in them.

> ⚠ SAFETY! CHILDREN NEED TO WEAR GLOVES WHEN HANDLING SOILS

Extension Activities

- Ask the children to find out the importance of air in soils to plants and animals.
- Find out the names of the gases in air.
- Give groups a set of cards as on the activity sheet on page 67. They should cut out the cards and put them under headings of *true*, *false* or *don't know*. Groups should compare their results with each other and come to agreement about the *don't knows*.

True or false?

Solids are always hard	Liquids can be poured	Gases can be poured
Solids take the shape of the container they are in	Toothpaste is a liquid	Toothpaste is a solid
A sponge is a solid	Air is made up of different gases	Gases can change into liquids if they are cooled
There is no air in a brick	Fire will go out if there is no air	There is air on the Moon
Solids can be changed into liquids if they are heated	Liquids can change into solids if they are heated	Gases spread out to fill the container they are in
Liquids spread out to fill the container they are in	Sand is not a solid	Helium is lighter than air

Cut out the statements above. With a friend, sort them into three piles.

? NOT SURE

Join with another pair and talk about your sorting. Come to an agreement if you can.

Literacy

Speaking and Listening

- Ask the children to find out about wind farms as an alternative source of energy. Are they a good idea or not? Consider the opinions of different people – see the display above for some ideas. Hold a debate about it – a chairperson, a speaker for and a speaker against it. Have a vote.
- Find out the effects of burning fossil fuels on the atmosphere. List alternatives. Groups should discuss different points of view. Make a display to show the different arguments.
- Make up a drama about the gases released by burning and chemical processes in factories, and how they attack plants when dissolved to make acid rain.

Reading and Writing

- Some rocks and all soils contain air. Tell the story of how rock changes into soil as on the activity sheet on page 69. Link with geography and compare soils in different localities. Use alternative ways to present the same information such as writing an account or a letter to another person, or a cartoon of how soil is made from rock.
- Observe bubbles carefully – look at their movement, colours and the reflected images inside them (images will be upside down). List interesting vocabulary under headings for parts of speech (verb, noun, adjective, adverb). Use these words to compose descriptive writing. Imagine what you might see inside a bubble – the window of a spaceship, a clown's nose, water in a river or puddles with oil in them.
- Make up similes and metaphors about bubbles – as shiny as polished glass; like a delicate drop of dew. Develop into longer pieces of writing.

- Make up characters to match the properties of a solid, a liquid and a gas. The solid could be a sponge, a brick or an iron nail; the liquid could be treacle, milk, beer or washing-up liquid; the gas could be oxygen, helium or hydrogen. Children should describe their characters, including as many properties as they can think of for them.

The birth of Sid Soil

The following statements tell how Ron Rock changed into Sid Soil. But they are in the wrong order. Cut them out, and then place them in the right order to tell the story.

	Rain fell and got inside him. It froze to make ice and expanded, then melted again and became smaller. After many, many years, cracks began to appear in him.He was becoming soft!
	Ron Rock was a hard character. No-one could break him up!
	Dead plants rotted around him and mixed up with him. At last he said 'Look at me! I've really changed! I think I shall call myself Sid Soil.'
	The cracks got bigger and Ron Rock began to crumble. He became smaller and smaller, and was surrounded by a pile of gravel. Some of the gravel became a fine powder. He was really mixed up!
	Ron Rock, a true rocker, lived quite happily on the surface of planet Earth surrounded by plants and animals – a really exciting place to be. He had a good life out in the Sun – swelling up in the day when he got hot and then shrinking at night when he cooled down.

Maths

Understanding Shape

- Use bubbles to study spheres and other 3-D shapes. Ask the children to write headings for different 3-D shapes and then list shapes around them under each heading. Name the 2-D shapes within each 3-D shape. Make up nets of different 3-D shapes. Why can't we make up a net of a sphere? See the display for ideas.
- Use a program to draw 2-D and 3-D shapes on the computer.
- Investigate properties of spheres. Find examples of different spheres around us. Introduce language; circumference (the perimeter), diameter and radius. Practice drawing circles in different ways, such as using compasses or a drawing pin and string. Split into equal parts and measure angles within it.

Measuring

- Revise previous work on capacity. Look at containers of different shapes and sizes. Estimate the capacity/volume of each. Check by pouring water in from a measuring cylinder.
- Learn about imperial and metric measurements. Convert millilitres to litres and vice versa. Sequence amounts from smallest to largest and place on a number line.
- Challenge children to think of different solutions to this problem:

  'How can we measure 4 litres exactly using only a 3l and 5l container and a tap to provide water? There are no marks on the containers.'

  Two solutions are:

  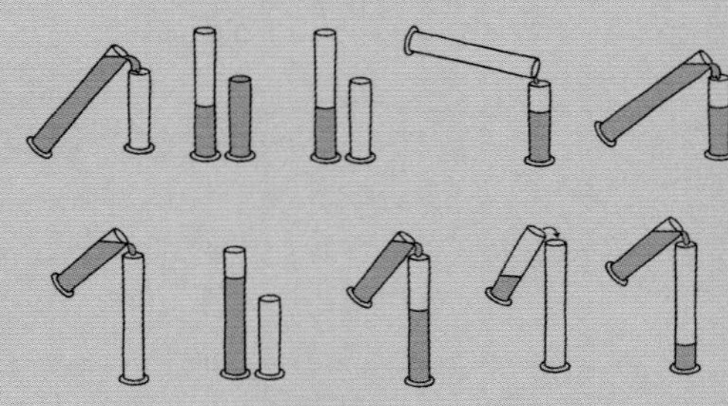

  Fill the 5L and pour into the 3L, leaving 2L in the 5L container. Empty out the 3L and pour the 2L into the 3L container. Fill up the 5L container again and use this to top up the 3L – leaving 4L in the 5L container.

  Fill the 3L and pour into the 5L. Fill the 3L again and pour into the 5L which will only take 2L more. That leaves 1L in the 3L container. Empty the 5L. Pour the 1L into it. Fill up the 3L and add it to the 1L already in the 5L container.

  There may be other solutions!
- When this has been solved, ask children to make up a similar problem using two different sized containers and an amount to measure. Children can become accomplished at these types of problems – ideal for homework and to drive parents crazy!
- Consider why the knowledge of volume is important to different people in their everyday lives – a car driver, a house removal company, a baker, a milkman, a cook, a hairdresser. Can children think of other people who need to consider volume of things?
- Complete the activity sheet on page 71. Children should be able to fill each container with rice or cereal and transfer to a measuring cylinder to find the volumes.

Put your popcorn here!

Make two popcorn containers.

1. Roll two A4 sheets of paper into cylinder shapes in these two different ways. Make each cylinder as large as you can. Tape the edges together.

2. Use another piece of paper to make a bottom for each one. Make sure no popcorn can drop out

Predict. Do you think your popcorn containers have the same volume as each other? Try filling them up with popcorn (or rice or cereal, if no popcorn is available) to find out.

Was it what you expected?

1. **What is the volume of each container? How can you find out?**

   Record what you do so others will know.

2. **Can you make a popcorn container with twice the volume?**

3. **Make different designs for popcorn holders. Find the volume of each and evaluate the designs. Which is the best and why? You could decorate some for an imaginary trip to the cinema.**

Design & Technology

- Look at how mobiles are constructed and how they balance. Make a mobile linked to gases – use wire, string and other materials to make a mobile that depicts different gases.
- Make different 2-D and 3-D shapes for blowing bubbles as shown on the activity sheet on page 73. Be warned that this is a messy activity! It's best to do it outside.

Art

- Look at art by artists who used shapes to inspire their designs, such as Henri Matisse (1869–1944) and Wassily Kandinsky (1866–1944). Use a graphics package to make up geometric shapes and arrange them into a picture. Give it a title.
- Look at pictures of hot-air balloons and the patterns and colours on them. Make up a group collage of a sky full of coloured hot-air balloons. One possible technique is layered tissue paper balloons with a glue glaze over them.
- Use air to blow pictures through a straw. Make a paint puddle on paper and blow through a straw to make a variety of designs.

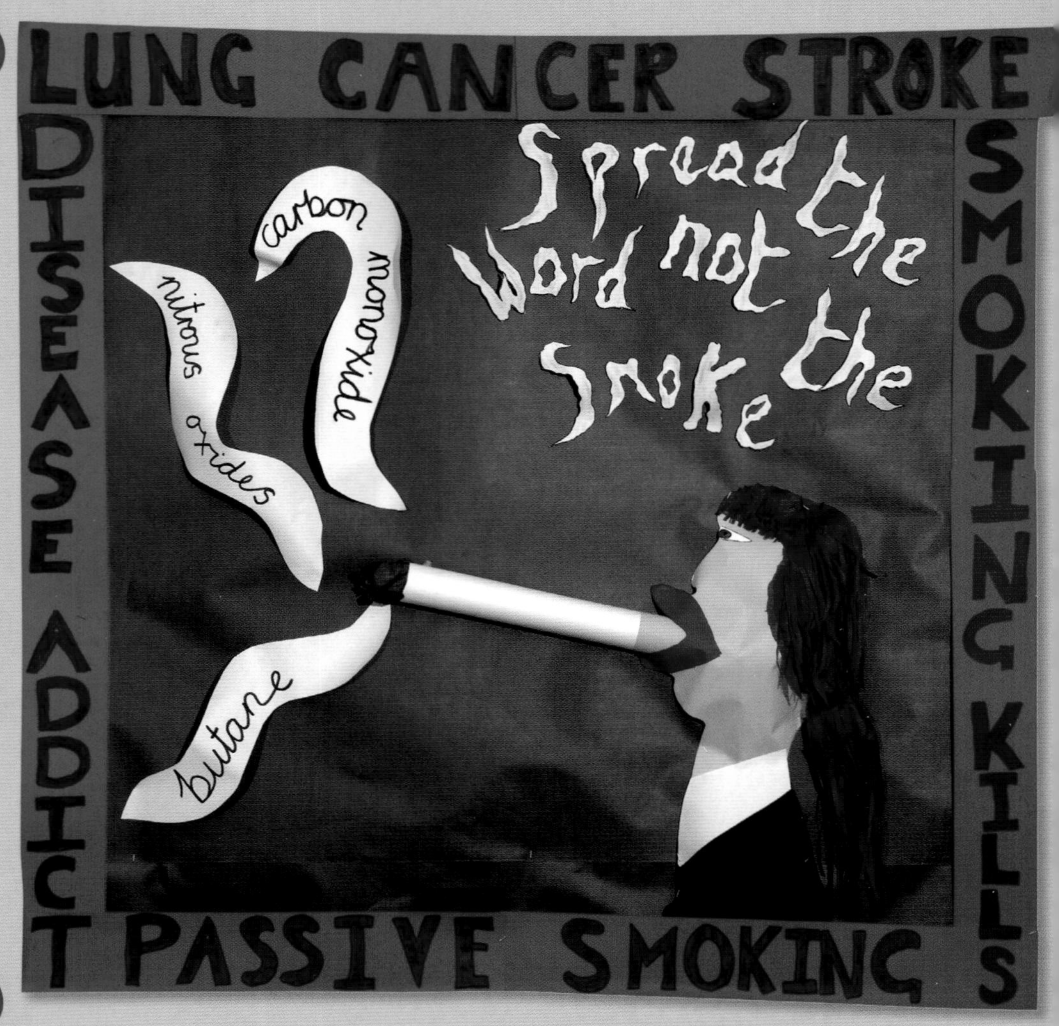

PSHCE

- Find out what gases come out of a burning cigarette. Make group pictures of someone smoking a large cigarette with the names of horrible gases coming out of it, as on the display. The person in the picture could be an evil character!

Music

- Learn to sing *I'm forever blowing bubbles* (tune by John Kellette, lyrics credited to Jaan Kenbrovin).
- Look at instruments that are blown to make sound.
- Ask children to devise sounds to go with artwork; their own or that of a famous artist – smoky music for LS Lowry and Claude Monet's paintings of pollution and fog; light airy music for pictures of floating balloons and so on.

Make up a strong bubble mixture like this:

Make a mess with bubbles!

1. Eight tablespoons of washing-up liquid
2. 1 litre of water
3. 1–2 tablespoons of glycerin or unflavoured gelatin to make stronger bubbles
4. Food colouring or powder paint for different coloured solutions.

Make a ring with your index finger and thumb and practice blowing bubbles through it to find out if the bubble mixture works well.

Make up or find some bubble blowing machines of different shapes.

These ideas might help you to decide on what to use and shapes to make!

Cut slits in the end of a wide plastic straw and fan out. Put in the bubble mixture and blow gently through the other end.

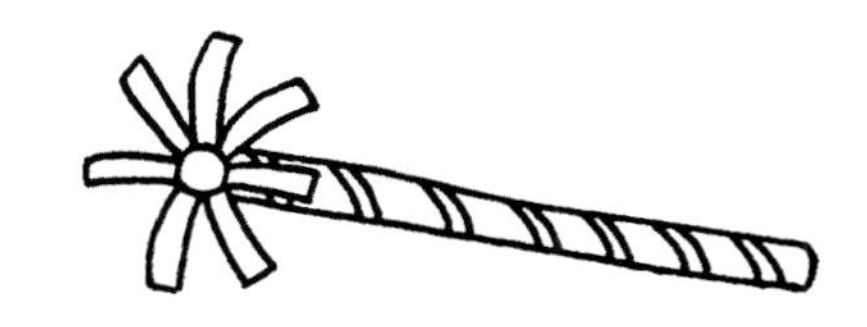

Tie a piece of string between two straws and dip them into the tray of bubble mix.

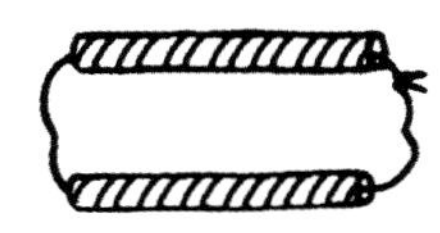

Bend a coat hanger into a circle, and then dip into a frying pan of bubble mix.

Use a plastic holder from a six-pack of fizzy drink cans. Six holes are best to make lots of bubbles.

1. **Blow a bubble inside a bubble**
2. **Make a chain of bubbles**
3. **Make coloured bubbles**
4. **Make the biggest bubble you can!**

History

- Look at how artists have depicted pollution at different times. The following pictures may be useful:

  LS Lowry (1887–1976): *Lancashire scene; Going to the match*

  Claude Monet (1840–1926): *Houses of Parliament, London, Sun breaking through the fog; The Thames at Westminster (Westminster Bridge)*

  JMW Turner (1775–1851): *The Fighting Téméraire*

- Consider styles. Paint own smoky picture in a particular style. Class could produce a joint effort for a large display or mural.
- Find out about Watt and Stephenson and the invention of the locomotive. How was it powered? Link to the burning of fossil fuels. Trace the development of the locomotive on a time line. Devise a play about the Rainhill Trials. Link to work about the Victorians.
- Read about the first hot air balloons, including the Montgolfier balloon flight. Read *Hot air: the (mostly) true story of the first hot-air balloon ride* by Marjorie Priceman (Caldecott Honor Book) or *Three in a balloon* by Sarah Wilson (Scholastic) about the first flight, which was made by three animals.

Geography

- Read *Atlantic free balloon race* by Thom Roberts (Avon) in which eleven-year-old Ned joins his eccentric relative Mr. T. Gray and a pet Kangaroo in a balloon race from New York to London. Find the two cities on a globe and on a map. Trace the journey between the two and describe the journey's scenery. Estimate the distance travelled and consider the dangers that might be encountered. Choose a location in the world for a balloon ride as on the activity sheet on page 75. It could be a contrasting journey to the one in the book. Describe it and imagine the hazards that could be encountered.
- Find out which gases cause acid rain. Learn about the effect on the environment and how it can be reduced. A useful website for information for children is www.ypte.org.uk
- Find out about air pollution problems in the area and how they are dealt with. Suggest ways of dealing with an imaginary situation where the air has become polluted.

PE

- Devise a group dance or movement to show a burning cigarette and what comes out of it. End with a slogan about smoking.

Up, up and away!

A wonderful present!

Imagine that you can go on a balloon ride to anywhere in the world.

Choose where you want to go.

Find out: **How far is it? What will you see on the journey? What is the place like?**

Balloons are often brightly coloured with interesting designs. Choose a design for yours that says something about you and where you are going, and complete the balloon above with your design.

NOW!

Collect information to let others know about your journey. Use the computer to make up a leaflet about your destination.

Assessment Ideas

In any activity the children carry out, whether through discussing, planning, doing or writing, there is an element of assessment. There are many ways to assess children – see the ideas below and the grid on page 77 for further suggestions. Knowledge-based assessments should use a variety of methods such as games, quizzes, drama and role play presentations, discussion of 'concept cartoons' and completing 'concept maps'.

- Concept cartoons are a useful tool in teaching and assessing. Each cartoon takes an everyday scientific idea about which three or more points of view are shown. For example, it could be a variety of views about how quickly objects fall. The cartoons encourage children to think carefully about what is being discussed and say which point of view they agree with and why. The cartoons generally portray a range of ideas which can be used to promote discussion of the children's own ideas and inform teachers what to teach and how to group children. For more information visit www.conceptcartoons.com
- Concept maps are also useful. The idea is to link nouns about a theme with arrows. The arrow shows the connection between the two words. For example:

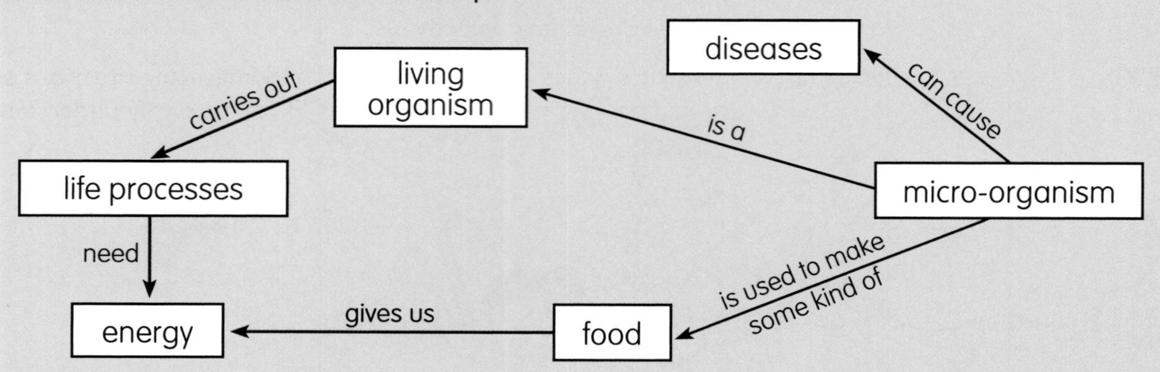

- Ensure that you have clear learning objectives for your lessons and that these are shared and understood by the children.
- Tell the children what the success criteria are and how they can achieve them.
- When marking children's work, highlight successes against the learning objective and write affirmative statements on the page, such as 'you can make a circuit' or 'you can name parts of the body'.
- Include time for assessment work in your daily and weekly planning. You may wish to conduct an end of topic investigation to access the children's level of knowledge and understanding.
- At the end of the topic, create a spreadsheet document to record the children's attainment against the objectives. Colour-code the cells: red for not achieved, orange for objective met and green for those who have exceeded expectations. This will produce an 'at a glance' reference to achievement and will highlight areas that need further work. Such documents could be handed on with other record-keeping to inform planning in subsequent year groups.
- Self-assessment sheets for children to complete are included on pages 78–80. The sheets cover areas of knowledge taught throughout the year. Children should be given their own sheets at the end of teaching a theme for them to colour in the objectives achieved. These could be colour-coded for those areas they think they know well/are uncertain about/do not know. The 'I can ...' statements of skills will be practised in different contexts throughout the year, so children need to make judgements on each one more than once, again at the end of each theme and they should write the date in the column when the skill is achieved. Use all the sheets alongside your assessments to inform reports and general assessment at the end of the school year.

Who Should Assess?

- Anyone involved with children's learning can assess, including parents and the children themselves. The most important thing is that the assessor knows what they are looking for and has the skills and knowledge to make these judgements. Children can assess each other – but they should always try to be constructive – what are the good points as well as the not so good?

HOW	TIPS
Observation of Children Working	Use this method when there is no written work as evidence, for example, when children are planning and discussing. Assess a single child or a group by questioning the children to clarify understanding.
Group Feedback	Use this method to clarify the understanding of 'quiet' children or those you are unsure about. Allow the 'listening' children to ask questions of 'presenters'. Ask questions of the children to gain a greater understanding of their learning.
Recording Children's Views During an Activity	Gather the children's opinions and ideas during activities. Ask the children to make their own recordings for you to listen to after the lesson.
Drama	This method is fun and non-threatening for children as they can 'show' instead of write their understanding of key objectives. Use role play to discuss issues and act out events and imaginary situations such as, 'inside a part of the body','in space' or 'inside the Earth' to clarify understanding of key concepts.
Concept Cartoons	Use at the beginning and/or at the end of lessons to clarify children's ideas.
Diagrams, Drawings and Photographs	Ask the children to draw ideas before teaching and at the end to compare understanding of concepts. Make/interpret concept maps before and after lessons/topics. Photograph the children's work before and after the topic is complete to compare.
Sort a Collection	Ask the children to sort a collection of objects/vocabulary related to the topic in different ways. This method is particularly good for Maths and Science, to pinpoint the children's grasp of skills and knowledge.
Make & Play a Game	Incorporate key concepts and vocabulary into games, for example, create questions that the children have to answer correctly before they move a space on a board game. Laminate games and retain for future use.
Devise & Answer Questions	Put questions in a box (generated by the teacher and the children) and ask the children to answer them over the course of the topic.
Interactive Display	Put questions on displays which highlight key concepts instead of labels. Add to the display as the topic progresses.
Types of Quiz	Create a true/false quiz on areas of knowledge and play this before and after teaching the topic to compare the children's responses. Quizzes can be oral or written by children or teacher.
Written Work	Writing is useful as evidence but be aware that this is not always the best way for children to demonstrate what they know or can do. Use different genres of writing.

Life Processes and Living Things

I know...

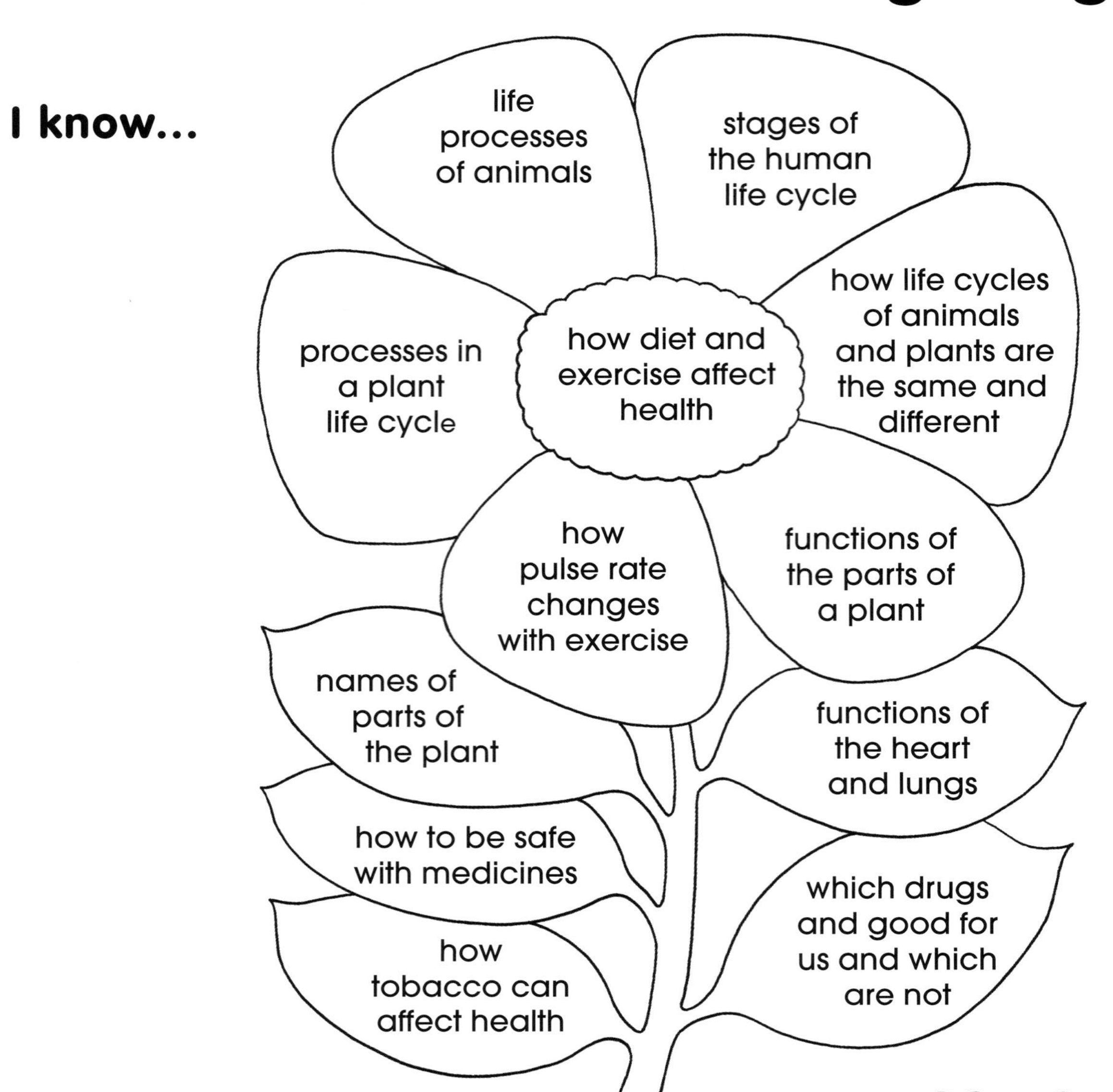

Scientific Enquiry

I can...

Skill	Date	Date	Date	Skill	Date	Date	Date
use scientific language in writing and speaking				make predictions			
ask different questions about things				give a reason for my prediction (hypothesise)			
suggest different ways to answer questions				share ideas with other children			
plan a method to answer my question				plan with others and listen to their ideas			
choose a way to record				decide on equipment needed			

© Folens photocopiable page • Self-Assessment • Belair Curricular-Links Science 5

Materials and their Properties

I know...

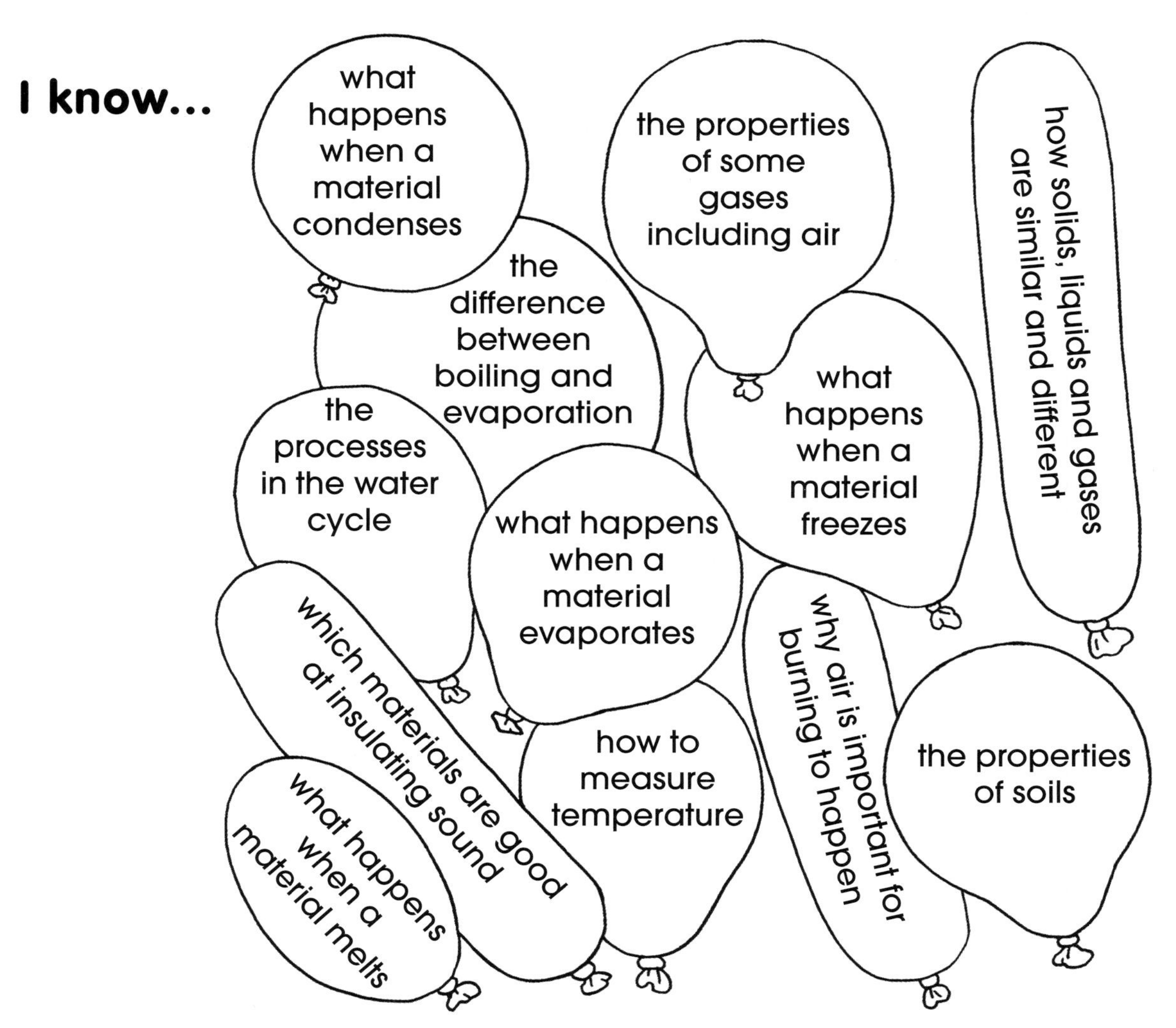

Scientific Enquiry

I can...

Skill	Date	Date	Date	Skill	Date	Date	Date
draw a table for results				use a computer to collect and store data			
carry out a fair test with help				use measuring equipment accurately			
carry out a fair test without help				decide if results can be transferred to a bar graph or pie chart			
explain how to make a test fair				draw a bar graph from data			
measure accurately				use data to draw a line graph with help			

Physical Processes

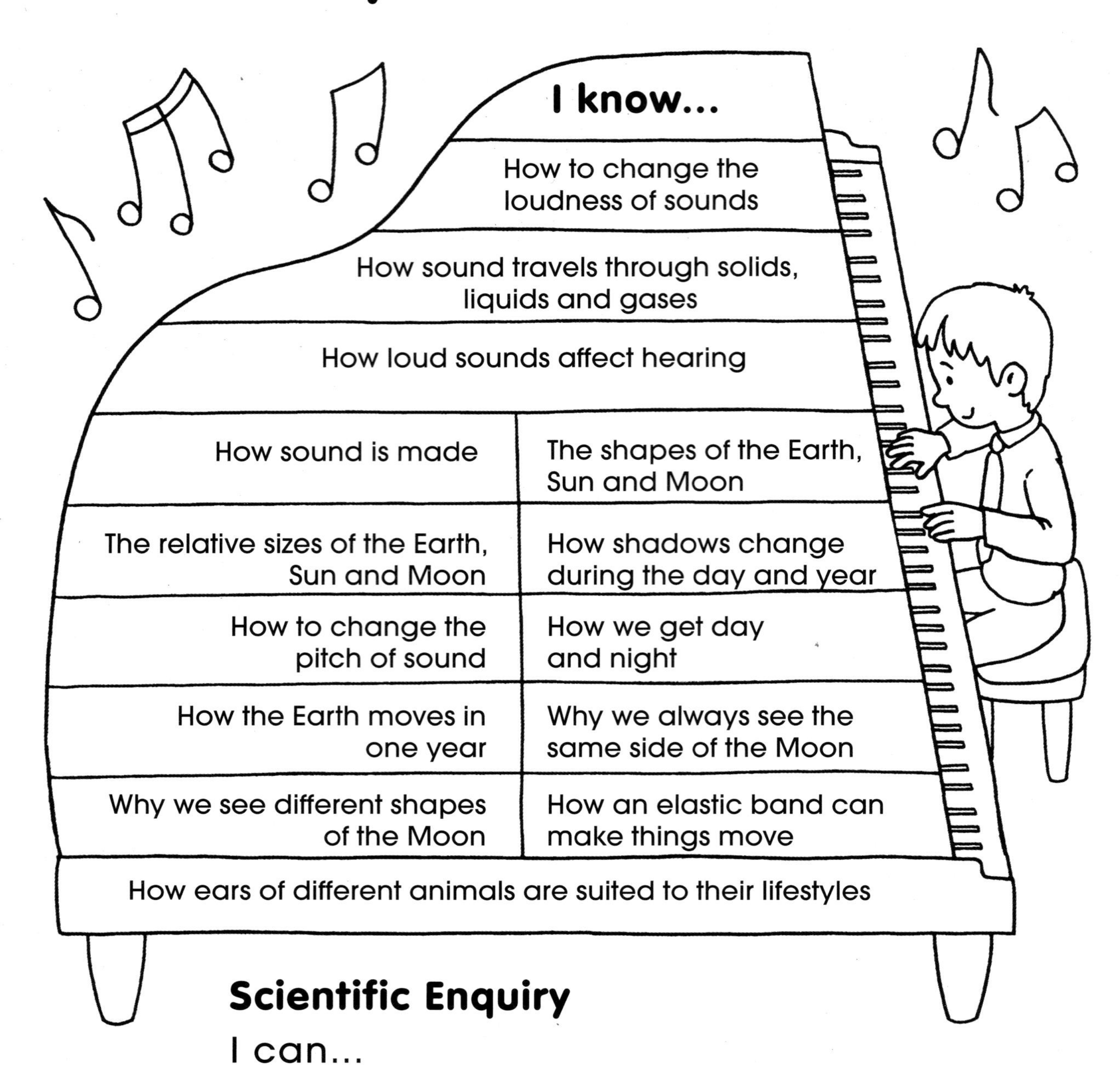

Scientific Enquiry

I can...

Skill	Date	Date	Date	Skill	Date	Date	Date
give detailed information about data I have collected				use results to make a generalisation (the …er, the …er)			
find patterns in data				explain results using scientific vocabulary			
find any results that do not match a pattern				decide on ways to improve my enquiry			
check results if I am unsure about them				decide on the best way to present an enquiry			

 © Folens photocopiable page